IGCSE
Study Guide

for Biology

Dave Hayward

HODDER
EDUCATION
PART OF HACHETTE LIVRE UK

The Publishers would like to thank the following for permission to reproduce copyright material:

All whole questions and part questions from IGCSE Biology examination papers are reproduced by permission of the University of Cambridge Local Examinations Syndicate.

1990: Paper 2 N, **p.126**, q.1. 1994: Paper 2 N, **p.113**, q.2. 1995: Paper 3 J, **p.68**, q.1. 1996: Paper 2 J, **p.72**, q.1; **p.129**, q.3 a, b. 1997: Paper 2 N, **p.18**, q.1; **p.43**, q.1; Paper 2 J, **p.95**, q.3; Paper 3 J, **p.106**, q.1 a, b. 1998: Paper 2 N, **p.4**, q.2; **p.21**, q.2; **p.103**, q.3; **p.108**, q.2; Paper 2 J, **p.31**, q.2; **p.92**, q.1 a; **p.97**, q.4; **p.115**, q.3; Paper 3 N, **p.33**, q.3. 1999: Paper 3 J, **p.7**, q.4; Paper 2 N, **p.60**, q.2. 2000: Paper 2 N, **p.9**, q.1; **p.85**, q.1; Paper 3 J, **p.48**, q.2. 2001: Paper 2 N, **p.2**, q.1; **p.86**, q.2; **p.118**, q.1; Paper 3 N, **p.21**, q.3 a; Paper 2 J, **p.101**, q.1; **p.111**, q.1; **p.120**, q.2. 2002: Paper 3 N, **p.73**, q.2; Paper 2 J, **p.78**, q.6; **p.87**, q.3. 2003: Paper 3 N, **p.14**, q.1; **p.128**, q.2; Paper 2 N, **p.36**, q.5; **p.124**, q.1. 2004: Paper 3 J, **p.16**, q.1 a, b; **p.80**, q.7.

J = June examination paper, N = November examination paper

Every effort has been made to trace all copyright holders, but if any have been inadvertently overlooked the Publishers will be pleased to make the necessary arrangements at the first opportunity.

Hachette's policy is to use papers that are natural, renewable and recyclable products and made from wood grown in sustainable forests. The logging and manufacturing processes are expected to conform to the environmental regulations of the country of origin.

Orders: please contact Bookpoint Ltd, 130 Milton Park, Abingdon, Oxon OX14 4SB. Telephone: (44) 01235 827720. Fax: (44) 01235 400454. Lines are open 9.00–5.00, Monday to Saturday, with a 24-hour message answering service. Visit our website at www.hoddereducation.co.uk

Cover photo Steve Knell/BBC wild
Typeset in Bembo 12/14pt by Pantek Arts Ltd, Maidstone, Kent
Illustrations by Art Construction
Printed and bound in Great Britain by CPI, Antony Rowe, Chippenham, Wiltshire.

A catalogue record for this title is available from the British Library

ISBN: 978 0 7195 7904 2

Contents

Introduction

Structure of the book

This text has primarily been written to support students in their study of Biology to IGCSE. The syllabus has two components, the Core and the Supplement. The Supplement defines the Extended curriculum. The Core is graded C to G whereas the Extended curriculum can be graded A★ to G. To differentiate between these components, sections of this book covering the Supplement are shaded. Wherever possible, this practice has also been extended to the questions, although this is not always straightforward as some questions involve material from both Core and Supplement.

Each topic starts with a list of **Key objectives**, which specifies the skills and knowledge you will need to have acquired during your study of the topic. The list can also serve as a checklist of your progress in the topic.

The syllabus also lists terms that you need to be able to define. These are provided in a section called **Key definitions**.

The knowledge you need for each topic is in the **Key ideas** section. It also contains very useful guidance on how to avoid common mistakes, and gives tips that will help you in the exam.

In each topic there are also questions. **Sample questions** have the answers given, sometimes as model answers, while other questions have been answered by an imaginary student to illustrate how answers of different quality are awarded marks.

The heading **Try this** indicates tasks and questions, many of which are from IGCSE papers or in the style of IGCSE questions. You should use these for practice and to assess your understanding and recall of the topic. All the answers can be found at the back of the book.

Preparing for the examination is primarily directed at those taking the external IGCSE examination, but much of the advice offered is also relevant to internal examinations (those set by your teachers).

How to use this book

The book is comprehensive. It contains all that is necessary to support the attainment of the highest grade for the short answer papers. It can be used for any one, or any combination of, the following purposes:

- as a textbook throughout the course
- at the end of each topic to provide reinforcement and assessment
- to prepare for internal examinations
- to prepare for the IGCSE examination.

To get the maximum value from this book it is strongly advised that you attempt to answer all the questions on paper and not in the book. Then you can repeat the exercises at intervals throughout the course. Sometimes you are asked to practise labelling diagrams – these can be traced or sketched.

I hope that you find this book a useful resource in your study of IGCSE Biology and that it assists you in gaining a commendable grade.

How do we learn?

We remember very little of what we have heard. We remember a little more of what we have heard and seen. We only really learn things thoroughly when we actually do things with the material – **active learning**. Not only is this more interesting and motivating for the students, but we actually understand, learn and remember things much better this way.

Active learning has always been promoted by good teachers whose lessons are not just 'talk and chalk'. In a practical subject such as Biology, there should be demonstrations with the active involvement of students who may take readings, discuss results and suggest further lines of enquiry. Practical work, usually in small groups, should ideally involve the students in the planning of the investigation. In any case, the students are actively involved in handling the apparatus and taking readings, and they usually go on to make calculations, draw graphs, deduce conclusions and evaluate their findings.

What you need to do

Study on your own should also be organised so that you are active. Simply reading through a textbook (or even this Study Guide) and hoping you will learn just does not work. The **Preparing for the examination** section at the end of the book gives further details about successful strategies.

Before you start to work with this book, you should ideally have a separate notebook or folder in which to record your work. You might wish to make the occasional comment in your normal exercise book, but there will not be space for the amount of extra work that should be done, and some schools may not allow these extra comments. Even though your separate notebook may only be seen by you, you should take the same pride in keeping it as if it were to be marked by the strictest teacher!

As your course proceeds, it will be useful to compare the notes in your exercise book with the topics presented here. There will be differences, but this does not mean that either your notes or this book is wrong. In fact, you will learn a lot from carefully comparing the two different versions and you will often find that the differences are alternative ways of presenting the same information. You should make a note of such points with comments about the differences and similarities.

How to answer different types of questions

● Calculations

● **Always show your working.** The first reason for this is that if you write down all your working, you are far more likely to work in the logical way needed to reach correct answers. Also, students often make errors early on in a multi-part question, and examiners try hard not to penalise more than once for the same error. If you continue on from an early wrong answer without making a further mistake, you will normally not lose any more marks as long as **the examiner can see clearly what you have done.** Do not expect the examiner to try and guess whether you worked on correctly.

- **Train yourself to set out work logically.** We are not all naturally neat and tidy in the way we work, but most people can improve with a little effort. Neatness certainly helps logical working and it is important to develop this habit throughout the course. You may think you can suddenly work logically in the exam, but it will not just happen if you have not practised it. Any calculations you do should be logically presented, and show all the steps of working.

- **Show the units.** Sometimes the question will make it easy for you and give the units. Sometimes you will be asked to state the units. Marks are often given for units, so develop the habit of thinking about the units and writing them down even when not asked for. Scientific quantities are meaningless without units. For example, it makes a lot of difference whether a volume is cm^3 or dm^3.

Graphs

- **Drawing graphs.** The axes should be labelled with units. The scales should fill more than half the space available in each direction. Think carefully about whether the origin should or should not be included. Do not use scales with awkward multiples such as 3 or 7 – there is no need to fill every part of the available space. The dependent variable is always on the y-axis and the independent variable is always on the x-axis. Points should be plotted carefully to an accuracy of 0.5 mm. This means using a sharp pencil to mark the point with a small cross or a circled dot. If the line of best fit is a straight line, carefully judge its position and draw one thin line with a ruler. If the line is a curve, it should be a single, thin, smooth line through the majority of the points. It must not be distorted to pass through every point.

- **Reading off graphs.** Again, you should work to an accuracy of 0.5 mm. Draw vertical and horizontal lines to the axes to show your working.

Descriptions and logical deduction

- **Logical thinking.** The important thing is not to abandon logic just because words are involved, not numbers. Many questions require step-by-step descriptions and/or deductions. You must be just as logical with words as you would be in working out a question with numbers.

- **How much do I write?** The space available is a rough guide but not a fixed rule. If you need much less space than that provided, think carefully about whether you have missed out something important. If you need a lot more space, you are giving details that the question has not asked for, or wasting time on extra detail for which the mark scheme will give no more marks. The value of the answer is always given in brackets next to the question. So, for example, a description with a mark of [3 marks] will require you to give three valid statements. Where a list is required, spaces are often given for the answers, for example: State three characteristics of living things.

1. _____
2. _____
3. _____

[3 marks]

Write only one answer on each line. If you make a list with more answers, the examiner will mark only the first answer in each line, even if others are correct. In other words, the examiner will not choose the correct answers from a list containing some right and some wrong answers.

● **Cloze passages** ● **Paragraphs where words have been left out.** You have to complete them, usually choosing words from a list given in the stem of the question. Read through the paragraph first, then fill in the easiest answers. Cross off the words you use from the list. This will leave you with a smaller choice for the hardest answers.

● **Matching pairs** ● **Questions where you have to match up names with descriptions, definitions or functions.** You are sometimes required to draw a line between the name and its function, for example:
  ● Identify the descriptions of parts of the respiratory system. Use a straight line to join the part with its description.

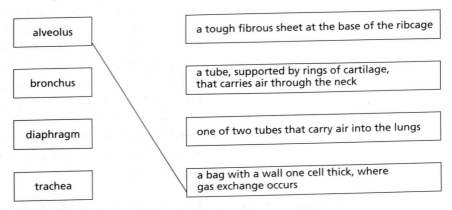

When answering this type of question use a ruler — curved lines can be ambiguous — and draw the line with a pencil (then, if you make a mistake, you can correct it). One has been done in the example.

● **Multiple choice** ● **You have a choice of answers.** When unsure of the answer, always try to eliminate some of the incorrect options as this increases the chance of choosing the correct response. Never leave any multiple choice answers blank, it is always worth having a guess, but this should only be done as a last resort. Candidates are not penalised for wrong answers.

Examination terms explained

The examination syllabus gives a full list of the terms used by examiners and how candidates are expected to respond.

Calculate	Give a numerical answer, generally showing the working out involved
Define	A precise statement is needed
Describe	State the main details, without an explanation
Discuss	Involves giving different points of view, or advantages and disadvantages
Explain	You must give reasons and/or underlying theory
List	You must give a series of points (usually as single words), keeping to the number specified in the question
Outline	State the main facts briefly, without going into detail
Predict	You are not supposed to know the answer from memory, but to deduce it, usually from information in the question
State	Give a concise answer; no explanation is needed
Suggest	This implies there is more than one acceptable answer or that candidates are expected to arrive at the answer using their general knowledge of Biology
What do you understand by	Give the definition and some additional explanation

TOPIC 1 Characteristics of living organisms

Key objectives
- To be able to list and describe the characteristics of living organisms
- To define the terms *nutrition, excretion, respiration, sensitivity, reproduction, growth* and *movement*

Key definitions

Nutrition	This involves feeding – obtaining nutrients for growth, energy and maintaining health. Plants make their own food, using photosynthesis, by obtaining simple nutrients (water, carbon dioxide) and light energy
Excretion	Getting rid of the waste products made by chemical reactions in cells
Respiration	The breakdown of food in cells to release energy
Sensitivity	The ability to sense and respond to changes in the surroundings. The term *irritability* is sometimes used instead of sensitivity.
Reproduction	Producing offspring. This prevents extinction of the species
Growth	An increase in the size, mass and complexity of an organism
Movement	In response to changes, e.g. the presence of a predator, to find food or a mate. Parts of plants move very slowly, e.g. to obtain more light for photosynthesis (achieved through growth)

Key ideas

Characteristics

There are seven characteristics that all living things, including plants and other organisms, show. You need to be able to recall and describe these. You may be given a picture of a living thing to study and then to identify which characteristics you can observe by watching it for a few minutes. Some of the seven would not be suitable as answers, e.g. growth, respiration, reproduction (these are not likely to be visible or observable in a short time span). Some non-living things, such as a car, may appear to show some of the characteristics – but not all of them.

Common misconceptions

Don't confuse respiration with breathing.

Don't use faeces or defecation as an example of excretion (faeces is undigested food – it has not been formed through metabolic processes). ■

> **Examiner's tip**
> ► Use a mnemonic to remember a list, e.g. MRS GREN stands for the first letters of the seven characteristics of living organisms. A mnemonic is often more memorable if you have made it yourself.

Sample question and answer

Sample question Name three characteristics of living things that you would expect an organism to show, other than irritability.   [3 marks]

Student's answer 1. movement ✓
2. reproduction ✓
3. sensitivity ✗

Examiner's comments *The first two answers are fine. However, the term sensitivity means the same as irritability, which has already been given in the question, so it did not earn a mark.*

● **Try this** The answers are given on **p. 138**.

1 Complete the following sentences about the characteristics of living organisms using only words from the list below.

excretion   growth   movement   nutrition   respiration   sensitivity

A living organism can be compared with a machine such as a car. The supply of petrol for the car is similar to (i) _____ and the release of energy when the petrol is burnt resembles (ii) _____ in a living organism.

This can bring about the (iii) _____ of the wheels.

(iv) _____ in living organisms is similar to the release of exhaust fumes by the car.   [4 marks]

TOPIC 2 Classification of living organisms

Key objectives
- To be able to define and describe the binomial system of naming species
- To be able to classify the five main classes of vertebrates
- To be able to list the main features used in the classification of flowering plants, arthropods, annelids, nematodes and molluscs
- To be able to list the main features used in the classification of viruses, bacteria and fungi, and their adaptation to the environment

Key definition

Binominal system	The system of classifying organisms using two names – genus and species – which are written in Latin

Key ideas

Classification

Classification makes the identification of living organisms easier – there are more than a million different species already identified! It involves sorting organisms into groups according to the features they have in common. The biggest group is a kingdom. There are five kingdoms, each with its own special and obvious features.

Bacteria – very small and single-celled, with cell walls but no nucleus.
Protoctists – single-celled, with a nucleus. Some have chloroplasts.
Fungi – many are made of hyphae, with nuclei and cell walls (containing chitin) but no chloroplasts.
Plants – multicellular organisms with the ability to make their own food through photosynthesis, due to the presence of chlorophyll. Their cells have walls (containing cellulose).
Animals – multicellular organisms that have to obtain their food. Their cells do not have walls.

Each kingdom is divided into smaller groups, which include genus and species. Organisms can exist in only one group at each level of classification. For example, an organism can only belong to one kingdom or one genus.

● **Try this** The answer is given on **p. 138**.

1 Make your own mnemonic with the letters B, P, F, P, A.

The binomial system of classification

This is a worldwide system used by scientists. Binomial means 'two names' – genus and species. The genus always has a capital letter, e.g. *Panthera leo* is the binomial name for lion.

> **Examiner's tip**
> ▶ When learning details about the classification of an organism, remember to identify what features are adaptations to its environment.

3 ●

Classification of vertebrates

Vertebrates are animals with backbones (part of an internal skeleton). Vertebrates are divided into five groups called classes. Details of each group are given in the table below. You only need to be able to describe visible external features, but other details can be helpful (see the 'Other details' column).

Vertebrate class	Body covering	Movement	Reproduction	Sense organs	Other details	Examples
Fish	Scales	Fins (also used for balance)	Usually produces jelly-covered eggs in water	Eyes but no ears, lateral line along body for detecting vibrations in water	Cold-blooded, gills for breathing	Herring, perch, shark
Amphibians	Moist skin	Four limbs, back feet often webbed to make swimming more efficient	Produces jelly-covered eggs in water	Eyes and ears	Cold-blooded, lungs and skin for breathing	Frog, toad, salamander
Reptiles	Dry, with scales	Four legs (apart from snakes)	Eggs with rubbery, waterproof shell – laid on land	Eyes and ears	Cold-blooded, lungs for breathing	Crocodile, python
Birds	Feathers, scales on legs	Wings, two legs	Eggs with hard shell	Eyes and ears	Warm-blooded, lungs for breathing, beak	Flamingo, pigeon
Mammals	Fur	Four limbs	Live young	Eyes, ears with pinna (external flap)	Warm-blooded, lungs for breathing, females have mammary glands to produce milk to feed young, four types of teeth	Elephant, mouse

● **Try this**   The answers are given on **p. 138**.

2 Figure 2.1 can be used to identify the main classes of vertebrate. Use the key to identify the main classes represented by the letters **A–E**.   [5 marks]

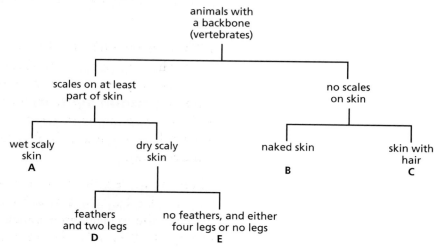

Figure 2.1

Sample question and answer

Sample question

Animals **A**, **B** and **C** are vertebrates.

A has a scaly skin, four legs and lungs.

B has hair, four legs and mammary glands.

C has a scaly skin, fins and gills.

Complete the table to show to which group of organisms each of the animals belongs. [3 marks]

Student's answer

Animal	Vertebrate group
A	reptile ✓
B	mammel ✓
C	fish ✓

Examiner's comments

The candidate has gained all three marks. The examiner allowed the second answer, although the spelling of mammal was not correct. Try to make your spellings correct — poor spelling can result in a mark not being awarded, especially if the word is similar to another biological word, e.g. meiosis and mitosis.

Classification of flowering plants

All flowering plants are multicellular organisms. Their cells have cellulose cell walls and sap vacuoles. Some of the cells contain chloroplasts.

They have roots, stems and leaves. Reproduction can be by producing seeds, although asexual reproduction is also possible.

There are two groups — monocotyledons and dicotyledons. The term cotyledon means seed leaf.

The main differences are shown in the table below.

Feature	Monocotyledon	Dicotyledon
Leaf shape	Long and narrow	Broad
Leaf veins	Parallel	Branching
Cotyledons	One	Two
Grouping of flower parts, e.g. petals, sepals and carpels	In threes	In fives

Classification of arthropods

Special features:

- They are invertebrates — they have no backbone.
- They have an exoskeleton which is waterproof — making arthropods an extremely successful group as they can exist in very dry places — they are not confined to water or moist places like most invertebrates.
- Their bodies are segmented.
- They have jointed limbs (the exoskeleton would prevent movement).

There are more arthropods than any other group of animals, so they are divided into classes. Figure 2.2 shows the differences between the four classes — insects, arachnids, crustaceans and myriapods. You only need to know about their external features.

Insects, e.g. dragonfly, locust

Key features:
- three pairs of legs
- usually have two pairs of wings
- one pair of antennae
- body divided into head, thorax and abdomen
- a pair of compound eyes.

Arachnids, e.g. spider, tick

Key features:
- four pairs of legs
- body divided into cephalothorax and abdomen
- several pairs of simple eyes
- chelicerae for biting and poisoning prey.

Crustaceans, e.g. crab, woodlouse

Key features:
- five or more pairs of legs
- two pairs of antennae
- body divided into cephalothorax and abdomen
- exoskeleton often calcified to form a carapace (hard)
- compound eyes.

Myriapods, e.g. centipede, millipede

Key features:
- ten or more pairs of legs (usually one pair per segment)
- one pair of antennae
- body not obviously divided into thorax and abdomen
- simple eyes.

Figure 2.2

● **Try this** The answers are given on **p. 138**.

3 **i)** Copy the diagrams of the insect, crustacean and arachnid and label the key features you can see.

ii) Copy the myriapod diagram and label features that are common to all arthropods.

Common misconceptions

Candidates are often confused by the different numbers of legs in insects, arachnids and crustaceans.

Candidates often state that insects have three legs instead of three pairs of legs, losing the mark through carelessness or haste. Be careful with your wording! ■

Classification of other groups of invertebrates

Although there are many groups of invertebrates, you only need to know details of the external features of annelids, nematodes and molluscs (Figure 2.3).

Annelids, e.g. earthworm	Nematodes, e.g. *Ascaris*	Molluscs, e.g. snail

Key features: ● elongated, cylindrical body covered with a mucus layer ● segmented body ● mouth and anus present ● bristles (chaetae) usually present ● may have a clitellum (reproductive structure).	Key features: ● elongated, cylindrical body ● body not segmented ● body pointed at both ends.	Key features: ● most have a shell, hardened by calcium carbonate ● have a muscular foot, used for movement or burrowing ● may have eyes on tentacles.

Figure 2.3

● **Try this**   The answers are given on **p. 138**.

4 Figure 2.4 shows the proportion of all known species in each of the main groups of organisms.

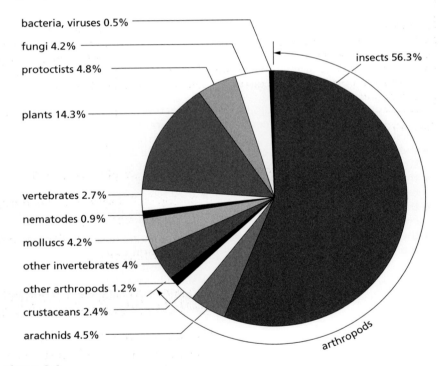

Figure 2.4

a) i) Apart from insects, which group of organisms in the diagram has the most known species?   [1 mark]

ii) Fungi are shown as a separate group of organisms. State two reasons why fungi are not classified as plants.   [2 marks]

continued

b) i) Use information from the pie chart to calculate what percentage of the arthropods are insects. Show your working. [2 marks]

ii) State **one** feature of insects which contributes to their success and explain how this feature is beneficial to the group. [3 marks]

c) 2.7% of all known species are vertebrates. Bird is one class of vertebrates.

i) State one feature which distinguishes this class from all the other vertebrate classes. [1 mark]

ii) State one external feature which birds have in common with fish. [1 mark]

d) It is estimated that 1.7 million species of organisms have been named. Use data from the pie chart to calculate the total number of plant species known. Show your working. [2 marks]

Classification of viruses, bacteria and fungi

Viruses, e.g. HIV	**Bacteria**, e.g. *Escherichia coli*	**Fungi**, e.g. *Mucor*
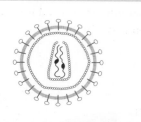		

Key features:
- they are very small (100 times smaller than bacteria)
- they do not have a typical cell structure
- they contain a strand of DNA or RNA
- they are surrounded by a protein coat called a capsid
- the only life process they show is reproduction (inside host cells).

Key features:
- they are small (1000 times smaller than a plant cell)
- they have a cell wall, made of a material other than cellulose or chitin
- they have a cell membrane and cytoplasm, containing glycogen granules
- they have no nucleus, with DNA in the form of a single, coiled chromosome
- some have a slime capsule
- some have one or more flagellae.

Key features:
- multicellular fungi are composed of hyphae (thread-like structures) which form a network called a mycelium
- their cell walls are made of cellulose or chitin
- cells merge together, with nuclei spread along the cytoplasm
- they do not produce chlorophyll
- they secrete enzymes to digest food outside the cells, absorbing the products
- some produce spores in a sporangium or a cap.

Figure 2.5

TOPIC 3 Using simple keys

Key objective

- To be able to use simple dichotomous keys based on easily identifiable features

Key ideas

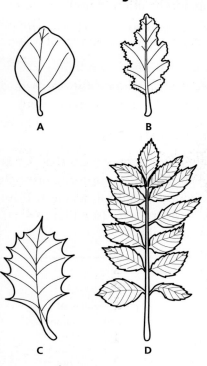

Keys are often used by biologists in the process of identifying organisms. You need to be able to use a dichotomous key – one which branches into two at each stage, requiring you to choose between alternatives.

You have already used a simple example when answering 'Try this' question 2.2. The choice was: scales on at least part of the skin or no scales on the skin. The example below also uses a simple dichotomous key.

● Try this The answers are given on p. 138.

1 Figure 3.1 shows single leaves from six different trees.

Use the key below to identify which tree each leaf comes from. Make a table similar to the one below and put a tick in the correct box to show how you identified each leaf. Give the name of the tree. Leaf **A** has been identified for you as an example.

1	**a** Leaf with smooth outline	go to 2
	b Leaf with jagged outline	go to 3
2	**a** Leaf about the same length as width	*Cydonia*
	b Leaf about twice as long as it is wide	*Magnolia*
3	**a** Leaf divided into more than two distinct parts	go to 4
	b Leaf not divided into more than two distinct parts	go to 5
4	**a** Leaf divided into five parts	*Aesculus*
	b Leaf divided into ten or more parts	*Fraxinus*
5	**a** Leaf with pointed spines along its edge	*Ilex*
	b Leaf with rounded lobes along its edge	*Quercus*

[4 marks]

Figure 3.1

Leaf	1a	1b	2a	2b	3a	3b	4a	4b	5a	5b	Name of tree
A	✓		✓								*Cydonia*
B											

Common misconceptions

Answers are often wrong for this type of question because the candidate has not worked through the key properly to select the answer, but has jumped to a statement that appears to fit the organism. ■

TOPIC 4 Cell structure and organisation

Key objectives

- To be able to state that most living organisms are made of cells
- To be able to identify and describe the structure of a plant cell and an animal cell (viewed using a light microscope)
- To be able to describe the differences in structure between typical animal and plant cells
- To be able to relate the structures seen under the light microscope in the plant and animal cells to their functions

Key ideas

Cellular structure of living organisms

Most living things are made of cells – microscopic units that act as building blocks. Multicellular organisms are made up of many cells. Cell shape varies according to its function (what job it does). Plant and animal cells differ in size, shape and structure (see Figure 4.1). Plant cells are usually larger than animal cells.

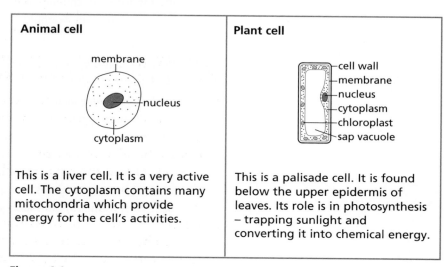

Animal cell	Plant cell
This is a liver cell. It is a very active cell. The cytoplasm contains many mitochondria which provide energy for the cell's activities.	This is a palisade cell. It is found below the upper epidermis of leaves. Its role is in photosynthesis – trapping sunlight and converting it into chemical energy.

Figure 4.1

Examiner's tips

- ▶ Practise labelling parts of a plant cell. Start from the outside (the cell wall) and work inwards. This is the correct order: cell wall, membrane, cytoplasm, chloroplast, nucleus, sap vacuole. The chloroplasts and nucleus are both held inside the cytoplasm.
- ▶ When labelling a plant cell, make the cell wall label line touch the outer line (cell walls are always drawn as a double line to show their thickness). The membrane label line should touch the inner line of the cell wall (when plant cells are turgid – firm – the membrane is pressed against the cell wall).
- ▶ Remember that animal cells contain only three main parts: membrane, nucleus, cytoplasm. Make yourself a mnemonic with **MNC**, or use this one: **M**ice **N**ibble **C**heese.

Parts of a cell

	Part	Description	Where found	Function
Animal and plant cells	Cytoplasm	Jelly-like, containing particles and organelles	Enclosed by cell membrane	• contains cell organelles, e.g. mitochondria, nucleus • chemical reactions take place here
	Membrane	Partially permeable layer that forms a boundary around the cytoplasm	Around the cytoplasm	• prevents cell contents from escaping • controls what substances enter and leave the cell
	Nucleus	Round or oval structure containing DNA in the form of chromosomes	Inside the cytoplasm	• controls cell division • controls cell development • controls cell activities
Plant cells only	Cell wall	Tough, non-living layer made of cellulose. It surrounds the membrane	Around the outside of plant cells	• prevents plant cells from bursting • freely permeable (allows water and salts to pass through)
	Sap vacuole	Fluid-filled space surrounded by a membrane	Inside the cytoplasm of plant cells	• contains salts and sugars • helps keep plant cells firm
	Chloroplast	Organelle containing chlorophyll	Inside the cytoplasm of some plant cells	• traps light energy for photosynthesis

Common misconceptions

Remember that animal cells never have a cell wall, chloroplasts or sap vacuoles (although they may have temporary vacuoles where food is stored).

Remember that not all cells have all cell parts when mature, e.g. red blood cells do not have a nucleus; xylem cells do not have a nucleus or cytoplasm.

It is not true that all plant cells contain chloroplasts, e.g. epidermis cells and root cells do not.

Remember that chloroplasts (structures or organelles) are different from chlorophyll (the chemical found in them). ■

● **Try this** The answer is given on **p. 138**.

1 Trace, copy or sketch the cells shown in the figure on page 10. Practise labelling both cells. Then do the same with other types of animal and plant cells.

Sample question and answer

Sample question Figure 4.2 shows a nerve cell. State the names of the cell parts **A**, **B** and **C**.   [3 marks]

Student's answer **A** cell wall ✗
B cytoplasm ✓
C nucleus ✓

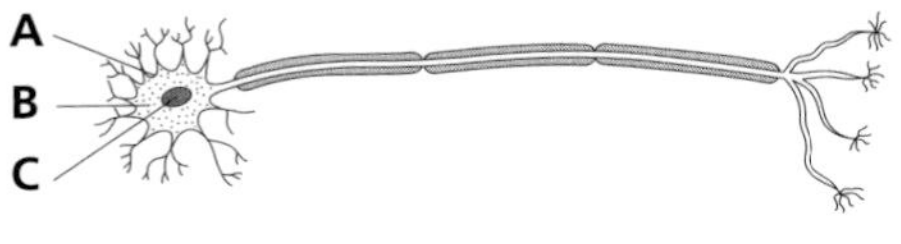

Figure 4.2

Examiner's comments *The first answer is wrong – a nerve cell is an animal cell, so it does not have a cell wall. The correct answer for **A** is cell membrane.*

TOPIC 5 Levels of organisation

Key objectives
- To be able to define *tissue*, *organ* and *organ system*
- To be able to relate the structures of tissues to their functions
- To be able to calculate the magnification and size of biological specimens

Key definitions

Tissue	A group of cells of similar structure that work together to perform a special function (job)
Organ	Several tissues grouped together to make a structure with a special function
Organ system	A group of organs with closely related functions

Key ideas

Figure 5.1 shows examples of cells and their functions in tissues.

Animal cells		
Ciliated cells – in respiratory tract	**Muscle cells**	**Red blood cells**
Special features: tiny hairs called cilia which can move mucus	**Special features:** cells merge together to form fibres that can contract	**Special features:** have no nucleus, contain haemoglobin
Function: waft mucus with bacteria and dust away from the lungs	**Function:** cause movement	**Function:** transport oxygen around the body

Plant cells	
Root hair cells	**Xylem cells**
Special features: the hair gives a large surface area	**Special features:** long, thin cells arranged end-to-end to form vessels (tubes). The cells lack end walls and cell contents such as cytoplasm and nucleus. The walls become lignified
Function: absorb water and mineral ions; anchor the plant firmly in the soil	**Function:** transport water and mineral ions from roots to leaves. Lignin provides strength for the stem and makes the vessels waterproof

Figure 5.1

Common misconceptions

Xylem and phloem tissue are often confused. Xylem carries water and mineral salts, while phloem transports sugars and amino acids.

Remember that in a vascular bundle in a stem, phloem is on the outside and xylem is on the inside. ∎

Example of annotation

Figure 5.2 shows the action of a phagocyte.

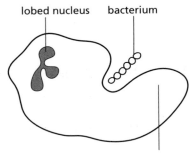

lobed nucleus   bacterium

cytoplasm forms pseudopodia
to surround and engulf
bacteria – enzymes are
released to digest and kill
bacteria

Figure 5.2

Size of specimens

- A microscope makes a specimen appear larger than it really is (it magnifies the specimen).
- You need to be able to calculate the magnification and also the actual size of the specimen.

Sample question and answer

Sample question With reference to a suitable named example, define the term *tissue*.
[3 marks]

Student's answer A tissue is a group of cells ✓ carrying out the same job. ✓

Examiner's comments *The answer needs three clear points to gain the 3 marks available: this candidate has not named a type of tissue (although this was the first instruction in the question) and has given only two points. Always use the marks shown in the margin to show you how many points to give. Avoid giving more than three; this would waste time that you need to answer other questions. Choose three statements to make before writing them down. The examiner will not select the best answers from a mixture of good and bad ones.*

● **Try this**   The answers are given on **p. 138**.

1   Identify parts **A**, **B**, **C** and **D** shown on Figure 5.3, and describe their main features and functions.

[12 marks]

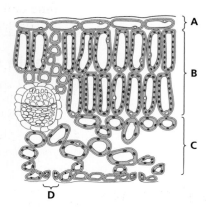

Figure 5.3

2 The diagram of a cow's eye shown in Figure 5.4 is magnified ×2.5.

Calculate the actual width of the eye, as shown between points **A** and **B**. Show your working.

[2 marks]

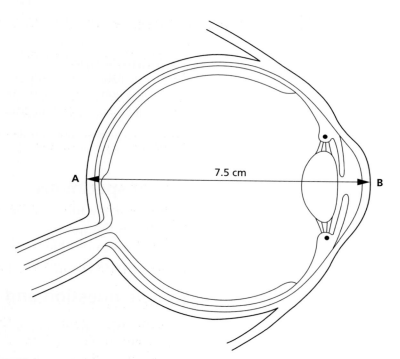

7.5 cm

Figure 5.4

TOPIC 6 Diffusion

Key objectives

- To be able to define *diffusion*
- To be able to describe the importance of gaseous and solute diffusion
- To be able to describe examples of diffusion in living organisms
- To be able to understand the factors affecting the rate of diffusion
- To be able to describe the importance of water as a solvent
- To be able to define *active transport*
- To be able to describe examples of active transport in living organisms

Key definitions

Diffusion	The movement of a substance from a region of its higher concentration to a region of its lower concentration down a concentration gradient
Active transport	The movement of a substance across a membrane from a region of its lower concentration to a region of its higher concentration against a concentration gradient, using energy

Key ideas

Examples of diffusion

Site of diffusion	Substance	Description
Alveoli of lungs	Oxygen	From the alveoli into blood capillaries
Alveoli of lungs	Carbon dioxide	From blood capillaries into the alveoli
Stomata of leaf	Oxygen	From the air spaces, through stomata into the atmosphere, during photosynthesis

You need to be able to state the factors that help diffusion to be efficient.

These are:

- Distance (the shorter the better), e.g. thin walls of alveoli and capillaries.
- Concentration gradient (the bigger the better). This can be maintained by removing the substance as it passes across the diffusion surface. (Think about oxygenated blood being carried away from the surface of alveoli.)
- Size of the molecules (the smaller the better).
- Surface area for diffusion (the larger the better), e.g. there are millions of alveoli in a lung, giving a huge surface area for diffusion of oxygen.
- Temperature (molecules have more kinetic energy at higher temperatures).

Common misconceptions

Don't confuse cell walls with capillary walls – animal cells do not have walls. Many candidates throw away marks referring to 'the thin cell walls of capillaries'. What they mean is 'the *walls of capillaries* are thin because they are only one cell thick'. ■

Importance of water as a solvent

- Most cells contain about 75% water.
- Many substances move around a cell dissolved in water.
- Many important reactions take place in water.

Active transport

Animals and plants rely on active transport to move some substances because the concentration gradient is not always the right way round for diffusion. However, cells need to provide energy to achieve movement by active transport. This energy is supplied through respiration using ATP. Mitochondria (cell organelles in the cytoplasm) control energy release. Respiratory poisons block energy release, so they can prevent active transport.

Examiner's tip
▶ There are two big differences between diffusion and active transport:
- direction of movement (down a gradient, or up a gradient)
- whether or not energy is needed for the movement.

Examples of active transport

Site of active transport	Substance	Description
Root hair cells	Mineral salts, e.g. phosphate	From soil into roots
Wall of small intestine (villi)	Glucose	From small intestine into blood plasma

● **Try this** The answers are given on **p. 139**.

1 Figure 6.1 shows part of a root.

a) Explain how the presence of root hair cells on roots enables the efficient absorption of water and minerals. [2 marks]

b) Root hair cells can absorb mineral ions by diffusion and active transport.
   i) Define the term *active transport*. [2 marks]
   ii) Explain why respiration rates may increase in root hair cells during the uptake of mineral ions. [1 mark]

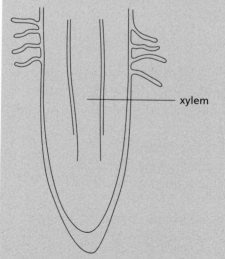
xylem

Figure 6.1

TOPIC 7 Osmosis

Key objectives
- To be able to define *osmosis*
- To be able to describe examples of osmosis in living organisms
- To be able to describe the effects of osmosis on plant and animal tissues
- To be able to show understanding of the concept of a *water potential gradient*

Key definition

Osmosis	The passage of water from a region of its higher concentration to a region of its lower concentration through a partially permeable membrane

Key ideas
- Plants rely on osmosis to obtain water through their roots.
- Plants use water as a transport medium (to carry mineral salts, sucrose and amino acids around the plant) and to maintain the turgidity of cells (their firmness).
- When young plants lose more water than they gain, cells become flaccid and the plant wilts.
- Fish living in salt water lose water by osmosis. They have very efficient kidneys to reduce water loss in urine.
- If we get dehydrated, water is lost from our red blood cells by osmosis. As the cells shrink, they become less efficient at carrying oxygen.

> **Examiner's tip**
> ► Osmosis is a special form of diffusion. It always involves the movement of water across a membrane.

Effects of osmosis on plant and animal tissues
- When placed in water, plant and animal cells will take in the water by osmosis.
- This is because there is a higher concentration of water molecules outside the cell than inside it.
- Plant cells become turgid, but do not burst because of their tough cell wall.
- Animal cells will burst, because they have no cell wall.
- The reverse happens when plant and animal cells are placed in concentrated sugar or salt solutions. This is because there is a higher concentration of water molecules inside the cell than outside it.
- Plant cells become flaccid and the cytoplasm is no longer pressed against the cell wall.
- Animal cells also become flaccid and their shape changes – they can become crenated.

Common misconceptions

Sugars and salts do **not** move by osmosis. Cell membranes prevent these substances entering or leaving the cell. ■

● **Try this** The answers are given on **p. 139**.

1 A potato was set up as shown in Figure 7.1 (left-hand side). The investigation was left for several hours. The results are shown on the right-hand side of the figure.

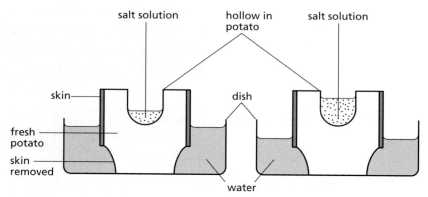

Figure 7.1

a) Describe what happened to i) the water in the dish and to ii) the salt solution in the hollow in the potato. [2 marks]

b) i) Name the process that is responsible for the changes that have occurred. [1 mark]

ii) Explain why these changes have occurred. [3 marks]

iii) Where does this process occur in a plant? [1 mark]

iv) What is the importance to the plant of this process? [1 mark]

Key definition

Water potential	The potential of water to move. Pure water and very weak solutions have a high water potential. Strong solutions have a low water potential.
Water potential gradient	Water will move down a water potential gradient from a high water potential to a lower water potential

Sample question and answer

Sample question Some sugar solution was collected from the phloem of a plant stem. Plant cells were placed on a microscope slide and covered with this sugar solution.

Describe what changes would occur to each of the three cell parts listed below if the sugar solution was more concentrated than the sap in the cell vacuole. [3 marks]

Student's answer **Sap vacuole:** it will get smaller ✓ because there is a higher concentration of water inside the cell, so the water will pass out of the vacuole by osmosis.
Cytoplasm: this will shrink because it is losing water? ✗
Cell wall: this will stop stretching and stop curving outwards. ✓

Examiner's comments *The first answer is correct, but this candidate has wasted time writing more than is needed — the question required a description, not an explanation. The second answer should give details about the way the cytoplasm comes away from the cell wall. In the third answer, details about the cell wall are not very well worded, but it is clear that the candidate understands what is happening.*

TOPIC 8 Enzymes

Key objectives

- To be able to define *enzyme, substrate* and *end product*
- To be able to describe the effects of changes in temperature and pH on enzyme activity
- To be able to describe the role of enzymes in the germination of seeds
- To be able to describe the use of enzymes in biological washing powders and in the food industry
- To be able to outline the use of microorganisms and fermenters to manufacture enzymes for use in biological washing powders

Key definitions

Enzyme	A protein that acts as a biological catalyst
Substrate	The chemical compound the enzyme works on
End product	The result of the reaction

Key ideas

Enzymes and reactions

Most chemical reactions happening in living things are helped by enzymes.

Most enzyme names end in –ase, e.g. lip*ase*, prote*ase*.

Enzymes usually speed up reactions, but some slow them down.

Some enzymes control reactions to build up molecules (synthesise them), e.g. starch phosphorylase:

$$\text{maltose} \xrightarrow{\text{starch phosphorylase}} \text{starch}$$

Others are involved in breaking down molecules, e.g. protease in digestion:

$$\text{protein} \xrightarrow{\text{protease}} \text{amino acids}$$

(See Topic 12 for other examples of enzymes.)

Enzyme molecules are **proteins**. Each molecule has a special shape and an active site – where the substrate fits.

Enzymes are very specific (each chemical reaction is controlled by a different enzyme). This is due to the shape of the active site.

For an enzyme to catalyse a reaction, the enzyme molecule and the substrate molecule need to meet and join together by means of a temporary bond.

Effect of temperature on enzymes

The optimum (best) temperature for enzyme-controlled reactions is around 37°C (body temperature).

Increasing the temperature above the optimum temperature slows the reaction down (see Figure 8.1). This is because enzyme molecules start to permanently lose their shape at high temperature. This deforms the active site, so the enzyme and substrate cannot fit together (so, no reaction). This effect is called denaturing. Most enzymes are **denatured** above 50°C.

19

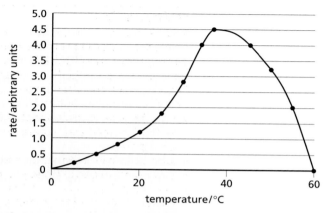

Figure 8.1 Graph showing the effect of temperature on the rate of an enzyme reaction

Common misconceptions

Enzymes are not denatured by low temperatures – they are just slowed down, and will work again when the temperature is suitable. Once an enzyme is denatured, the damage is permanent. ■

Effect of pH on enzymes

The pH of a solution is how acidic or alkaline it is. Most enzymes have an optimum pH (at which they work best) – usually around neutral (pH 7), but there are some exceptions:

- pepsin, pH 2.0 – in the stomach, with hydrochloric acid
- salivary amylase, pH 6.8 – in the mouth
- catalase, pH 7.6 – in plants, e.g. potato
- pancreatic lipase, pH 9.0 – in the duodenum.

The 'wrong' pH slows down enzyme activity, but this can usually be reversed if the optimum pH is restored.

An extreme pH can denature enzymes – the active site is deformed permanently.

● **Try this**   The answers are given on **p. 139**.

1 Make a table of enzymes you have learned about. Use this structure:

Name of enzyme	Substrate (what the enzyme works on)	End product(s)	Other details (e.g. where reaction happens, optimum pH)

Examiner's tips

▶ You need to be able to state the definition of an enzyme – learn it by heart. Do this by reading the definition, then covering it up and writing it out. Then check it is correct. Repeat this three or four times. Test yourself again 24 hours later.

▶ Enzyme questions often involve plotting a set of results on a graph. Remember the key points for drawing a graph:
  • plot the independent variable (the figures you control) on the x– (horizontal–) axis – these are the figures that usually go up in even stages
  • label both axes with a title and units
  • plot points in pencil (then you can change any mistakes)
  • join the points with a line (this can be a curve).

▶ If you are instructed to predict a result using a graph, draw on the graph to read off the answer. Remember to state the units.

● **Try this** The answers are given on **p. 139**.

2 Six identical samples containing a mixture of starch and amylase in water were kept at different temperatures, and the time taken for the starch to be digested was measured. The results are shown in the table.

Temperatures at which samples were kept/°C	Time for starch to be digested/ minutes
15	32
20	18
30	7
35	3
40	10
50	35

a) Plot a graph of these results. [3 marks]

b) i) Describe how the time taken for the starch to be digested could be determined. [2 marks]

   ii) At which temperature was the starch digested most rapidly? [1 mark]

   iii) Describe the relationship between temperature and the rate of starch digestion. [2 marks]

c) Similar samples were set up and kept at 10°C and 60°C. The starch in these samples was not fully digested after an hour. Both of these samples were then kept at 35°C. Suggest and explain the effect of these changes in temperature on starch digestion.
   i) Sample changed from 10°C to 35°C. [2 marks]
   ii) Sample changed from 60°C to 35°C. [2 marks]

3 a) Adult female mosquitoes feed on the blood of mammals. They produce a protein-digesting enzyme called trypsin.
   i) Explain why an adult female mosquito would need trypsin. [2 marks]

   ii) State the product that would be present in the gut of the mosquito if trypsin had been active. [1 mark]

   iii) State **one** use of this product in the body of an organism such as a mosquito. [1 mark]

continued

Scientists have found a way of introducing a hormone into mosquitoes to switch off the trypsin secretion.

b) Suggest how this treatment would affect adult female mosquitoes.

[2 marks]

c) Enzymes such as trypsin are easily damaged. Suggest **two** ways of damaging an enzyme. [2 marks]

Role of enzymes in germinating seeds

Seeds contain stored food in the cotyledons to provide energy and materials for growth. This is usually in the form of starch – a large, insoluble molecule that keeps the food immobile (stops it moving). For the seed to make use of it, the starch needs to be changed into a soluble molecule (sugar), a process controlled by the enzyme amylase. Water is needed (this enters the seed through its micropyle), and warmth helps speed up the process of starch breakdown (recall the effect of temperature on enzymes, page 19).

Use of enzymes in biological washing powders

Biological washing powders contain protease and lipase to remove protein stains and fat/grease from clothes. This makes the washing powder more effective than detergent alone, especially at lower temperatures. This saves energy (no need to boil water), but if the temperature is too high the enzymes will be denatured.

Use of microorganisms and fermenters to manufacture enzymes for use in biological washing powders

Two types of microorganism can be used to manufacture enzymes – **fungi** and **bacteria**. The fermenter (Figure 8.2) is a large, sterile container with a stirrer, a pipe to add feedstock (molasses or corn-steep liquor), and air pipes to blow air into the mixture. The microorganisms are added and the liquid is maintained at around 26°C and a pH of 5–6. The enzymes produced by the microorganisms may be extracellular or intracellular. **Extracellular** enzymes are extracted from the feedstock by filtering. To extract **intracellular** enzymes the microorganisms are filtered from the feedstock, then crushed and washed with water. The enzymes are now in solution.

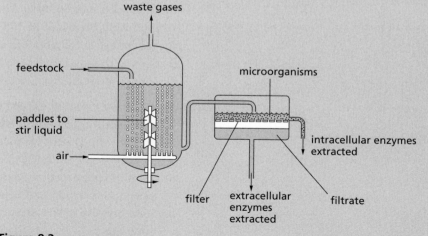

Figure 8.2

Use of enzymes in the food industry

Process	Use of enzymes
Baking	Enzymes in yeast convert sugar to ethanol and carbon dioxide. The carbon dioxide makes the bread dough rise
Brewing	Enzymes in yeast convert sugar to ethanol and carbon dioxide. The ethanol makes the drink alcoholic; carbon dioxide gives the drink its fizz
Cheese making	The enzyme rennin, extracted from cows' stomachs, is used to clot milk. Rennin can now be made using genetically engineered bacteria
Making baby foods	Trypsin (a protease) is used to predigest baby foods

Sample question and answer

Sample question   Figure 8.3 shows a box of biological washing powder. Study the information on the box.

a) Explain why:

i) the presence of protease and lipase would make the washing powder more effective than ordinary detergent   [3 marks]

ii) the powder should not be used in boiling water.   [2 marks]

b) Silk is a material made from protein. Explain why the biological washing powder should not be used to wash silk clothes.

[2 marks]

Figure 8.3

Student's answer   **a) i)** Protease and lipase are enzymes, ✓ so they would break down stains ✓ better than ordinary detergent.

ii) You could burn your hands when taking the clothes out. ✗

b) There is protease ✓ in the biological washing powder. This would digest the protein ✓ in the silk so the clothes would get spoiled.

Examiner's comments   *a) i) There are three marks available in this section. The candidate has made two valid statements, but has not given enough detail about what the enzymes digest (protease breaks down protein; lipase breaks down fats).*

ii) The candidate does not answer the question — the statement needs to be related to the properties of enzymes — they are denatured at high temperatures.

b) This is a good response, gaining both the available marks.

TOPIC 9 Nutrition and nutrients

Key objectives

- To be able to define *nutrition*
- To be able to list the chemical elements that make up carbohydrates, fats and proteins
- To be able to describe the synthesis of large molecules from smaller base units
- To be able to describe food tests for starch, reducing sugars, fats and proteins
- To be able to list the main sources and describe the importance of the main foodstuffs
- To be able to describe the deficiency symptoms for calcium, iron, vitamin C and vitamin D
- To be able to describe the use of microorganisms in the food industry
- To be able to describe the uses, benefits and health hazards associated with food additives

Key definition

Nutrition   Obtaining the organic substances and mineral ions from which organisms gain their energy and the raw materials for growth and tissue repair

Key ideas   Main nutrients

Nutrient	Elements present	Use in the body	Good food sources
Carbohydrate	Carbon, hydrogen, oxygen	Source of energy	Rice, potato, yam, cassava, bread, millet, sugary foods (cake, jam, honey)
Fat/oil (oils are liquid at room temperature, but fats are solid)	Carbon, hydrogen, oxygen (but lower oxygen content than carbohydrates)	Source of energy (twice as much as carbohydrate), insulation against heat loss, some hormones, cell membranes, insulation of nerve fibres	Butter, milk, cheese, egg yolk, animal fat, groundnuts (peanuts)
Protein	Carbon, hydrogen, oxygen, nitrogen, sometimes sulphur or phosphorus	Growth, tissue repair, enzymes, some hormones, cell membranes, hair, nails. Can be broken down to provide energy	Meat, fish, eggs, soya, groundnuts, milk, Quorn, cowpeas

Examiner's tips
- ▶ Carbohydrates, fats and proteins are all made up of the elements carbon, oxygen and hydrogen.
- ▶ Proteins also always contain nitrogen.
- ▶ One way of remembering the elements in carbohydrate is to look at its name: **C**arb **O** **H**ydrate (carbon, oxygen, hydrogen).

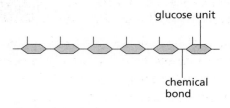

glucose unit

chemical bond

Figure 9.1 Carbohydrate

Large carbohydrate molecules such as starch, glycogen and cellulose are made up of long chains of smaller units – monosaccharides such as glucose – held together by chemical bonds (Figure 9.1).

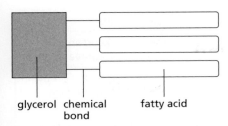

glycerol chemical   fatty acid
          bond

Figure 9.2 Fat

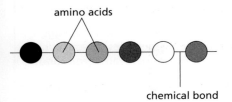

amino acids

chemical bond

Figure 9.3 Protein

Fats are made up of three units of fatty acids chemically bonded to one glycerol unit (Figure 9.2).

Proteins are made of long chains of amino acids chemically bonded together (Figure 9.3). As there are about 20 different amino acids, their pattern in the chain can be quite complex, and the molecules can be very large.

Food tests

You need to be able to describe the tests for starch, reducing sugars, protein and fats. Make sure you also learn the colour change for a positive result.

Food tested	Name of test	Method	Positive result
Starch	Starch test (very original!)	Add a few drops of iodine solution to a solution of the food	Blue/black coloration
Reducing sugar	Benedict's test	Add an equal amount of Benedict's solution to a solution of the food. Boil carefully	A succession of colour changes: from turquoise to pale green, pea green, orange, brick red. The further the colour change is along the gradient, the more reducing sugar is present
Protein	Biuret test	Add an equal amount of sodium hydroxide to a solution of the food. Mix carefully. Then add a few drops of 1% copper sulphate, without shaking the mixture	Violet halo
Fats	Emulsion test	Dissolve the food in ethanol. Pour the solution into a clean test tube of water	White emulsion

Common misconceptions

It is not true that several of the food tests require heating. The only food test that needs heating is the Benedict's test. ◼

Other nutrients

Vitamins and minerals, although needed only in small quantities, are important for maintaining good health. A shortage can result in a deficiency disease. You only need to know vitamins C and D, and the minerals calcium and iron. Fibre (roughage) is needed in much larger quantities. Although it has no nutritional value to us, the table on page 26 shows why we need it in the diet. Don't forget that water is also a vital part of our dietary requirements.

Nutrient	Function	Effect of deficiency	Good food sources
Vitamin C	Needed to maintain healthy skin and gums	Scurvy – bleeding under skin, bleeding gums	Citrus fruits, blackcurrants, cabbage, tomato, guava, mango
Vitamin D	Needed to maintain hard bones. Helps in absorption of calcium from small intestine	Rickets – soft bones that become deformed. Sufferers may be bow-legged	Milk, cheese, egg yolk, fish-liver oil. Can be made in the skin when exposed to sunlight
Calcium	Needed to form healthy bones and teeth and for normal blood clotting	Rickets and slow blood clotting	Milk, cheese, fish
Iron	Needed for formation of haemoglobin in red blood cells	Anaemia – constant tiredness, lack of energy	Red meat, liver, kidney, eggs, green vegetables (spinach, cabbage, cocoyam, groundnut leaves), chocolate
Fibre	This is cellulose. It adds bulk to undigested food passing through the intestines, maintaining peristalsis	Constipation. Long-term deficiency can lead to bowel cancer	Vegetables, fruit, wholemeal bread
Water	Formation of blood, cytoplasm, as a solvent for transport of nutrients and removal of wastes (as urine). Enzymes only work in solution	Dehydration	Drinks, fruit, vegetables

Sample question and answer

Sample questions and student's answers

The table shows the carbohydrate content of some vegetables.

Vegetable	Total carbohydrate g/100 g	Starch g/100 g	Fibre g/100 g
Beans	15.1	9.3	3.5
Broccoli	1.1	trace	2.3
Cabbage	4.1	0.1	2.4
Carrots (boiled)	4.9	0.2	2.5
Chickpeas	18.2	16.6	4.3
Onions	3.7	trace	0.7
Peas (frozen, boiled)	9.7	4.7	5.1
Potato (boiled)	17.0	16.3	1.2
Sweet potato (boiled)	20.5	8.9	2.3
Tomatoes (raw)	3.1	trace	1.0

a) Name the chemical elements present in a carbohydrate.
C, H, O ✗ [1 mark]

b) State which vegetable in the table contains:
 i) the highest proportion of total carbohydrate
 sweet potato ✓ [1 mark]
 ii) the highest proportion of fibre.
 peas ✓ [1 mark]

continued

c) Total carbohydrate is calculated as the sum of starch and sugars in the vegetable.

   i) Name the vegetable that contains the highest proportion of sugar per 100 g vegetable.

   sweet potato ✓ [1 mark]

   ii) Calculate the amount of sugar present in 500 g of the vegetable named in (i). Show your working.

   20.5 − 8.9 = 11.6
   11.6 × 5 ✓ = 58 ✗ [2 marks]

Examiner's comments *Most of the answers were good, but this candidate made two silly errors:*

a) *Don't use abbreviations such as symbols when you are asked to name elements.*

c) ii) *Remember to state the units when giving the answer to a calculation. This candidate gained one mark for showing the correct working for the calculation, but lost the second mark because of the lack of units – which should have been 'g' (grams).*

Use of microorganisms in the food industry

Process	Use of microorganism
Baking	Yeast is mixed with flour, some sugar and water to make dough. The dough is kept warm to allow the yeast to respire the sugar, producing pockets of carbon dioxide. These make the dough rise. When the bread is baked, the yeast is killed
Brewing	Yeast respires sugar to form ethanol and carbon dioxide. The source of the sugar is usually fruit juice or grain. The ethanol produced makes the drink alcoholic; carbon dioxide gives the drink its fizz. The process is called fermentation
Yoghurt making	Bacteria (usually *Streptococcus thermophilus* and *Lactobacillus bulgaricus*) are used to ferment milk at 46°C. As a result, lactic acid is produced (as fermentation progresses, the pH drops). The lactic acid makes the milk coagulate. The temperature is then reduced to 5°C to prevent further bacterial action. The whole process is carried out in sterile conditions
Single-cell protein (scp)	This is protein produced by microorganisms such as bacteria, fungi (e.g. yeast) or unicellular algae in a fermentation vessel. While the product ('pruteen') contains 72% protein, it does not taste very nice and is expensive to produce. An alternative is Quorn. This is mycoprotein made from a filamentous fungus (so, strictly, not single-cell protein). It is a healthy alternative to meat because it contains 12.2% protein, and has a low fat content and 6% fibre

Uses, benefits and health hazards associated with food additives

Food additives are used for a number of purposes, mainly to extend the life of processed foods so they can be transported, stored or kept on the shop shelf for longer, maintain a standard quality, and make the products more attractive to the consumer. Additive groups include antioxidants, colourings, flavourings and preservatives.

continued

Antioxidants – stop foods reacting with oxygen, which may spoil the taste of the food or change its colour.

Colourings – improve the appearance of the food. But some colourings can be hazardous, e.g. sunset yellow, added to some orange drinks, can cause hyperactivity in children as well as triggering allergic reactions such as asthma. Egg-laying chickens are sometimes fed grain containing colourings to make the egg yolks a brighter colour.

Flavourings – enhance the taste of food. Monosodium glutamate is often present in processed food and is popular in Chinese cookery. Often the flavour is due to a chemical additive, rather than the real taste of the food product. Sugar is one of the commonest flavourings, often present in savoury foods as well as cakes and biscuits. Artificial sweeteners, such as aspartame, are present in 'diet' fizzy drinks. They add to the drink's sweetness without adding calorific value. Normal fizzy drinks can contain up to five spoons of sugar per can – risking obesity and tooth decay for consumers who drink them regularly.

Preservatives – give processed foods a longer shelf life by preventing the growth of microorganisms such as bacteria and fungi that would otherwise make the food go bad and cause food poisoning. Processed meat, jam and fruit juices often contain preservatives, e.g. sulphur dioxide or sodium nitrite. Sulphur dioxide can destroy vitamin B_1, while sodium nitrite is suspected of being a carcinogen.

● **Try this**   The answers are given on **p. 139**.

1 Learn the groups of food preservatives listed above. For each group, state:

i) its function in processed food

ii) one advantage of its use

iii) one disadvantage of its use.

TOPIC 10 Plant nutrition

Key objectives

- To be able to define *photosynthesis*
- To be able to state the word equation for photosynthesis
- To be able to describe the process of photosynthesis
- To be able to identify the cellular and tissue structure of a leaf and relate the features to their functions
- To be able to describe the importance of nitrate and magnesium ions
- To be able to describe the uses, and the dangers of overuse, of nitrogen fertilisers
- To be able to state the symbol equation for photosynthesis
- To be able to define the term *limiting factor*
- To be able to interpret the effects of light intensity and carbon dioxide on photosynthesis
- To be able to explain the use of carbon dioxide enrichment, optimum light and optimum temperatures in greenhouse systems
- To be able to explain the effects of nitrate and magnesium ion deficiencies on plant growth

Key definitions

Photosynthesis	The building up of food molecules in plants from carbon dioxide and water, using light energy
Limiting factor	The external factor which restricts the effects of others. When a number of factors are needed, it is the one in shortest supply

Key ideas

The equation for photosynthesis

Word equation:

$$\text{carbon dioxide} + \text{water} \xrightarrow[\text{chlorophyll}]{\text{light}} \text{glucose} + \text{oxygen}$$

Symbol equation:

$$6CO_2 + 6H_2O \xrightarrow[\text{chlorophyll}]{\text{light}} C_6H_{12}O_6 + 6O_2$$

Note: the glucose produced is converted to starch for storage in the leaf.

The equation shows that the raw materials for photosynthesis are carbon dioxide, water and light energy. The products are glucose (starch) and oxygen.

> **Examiner's tip**
> ► Don't write an equation with a mixture of words and symbols. For Core, you only need to learn the word equation.

Common misconceptions

Candidates often suggest that photosynthesis happens during the day and respiration happens at night. The first part of the sentence is correct, but the second part is wrong: respiration happens all the time (in both plants and animals). ■

The process of photosynthesis

- Green plants take in carbon dioxide through their leaves. This happens by diffusion.
- Water is absorbed through plants' roots by osmosis and transported to the leaf through xylem vessels.
- Chloroplasts, containing chlorophyll, are responsible for trapping light energy. This energy is used to break up water molecules and then to bond hydrogen and carbon dioxide to form glucose.
- Glucose is usually changed to sucrose for transport around the plant, or to starch for storage.
- Oxygen is released as a waste product, or used by the plant for respiration.

Testing a leaf for starch

This is done to find out if photosynthesis has taken place. Starch is stored in plant leaves as a product of photosynthesis. The starch test does not work by placing iodine solution on fresh leaves: it is not absorbed.

You need to be able to describe the starch test and the reasons for each stage. There are also some important safety points.

Stage	Reason	Safety points
Boil the leaf in water	To kill the leaf – this makes it permeable	Danger of scalding
Boil the leaf in ethanol	To decolorise the leaf – chlorophyll dissolves in ethanol	No naked flames – ethanol is highly flammable
Rinse the leaf in water	Boiling the leaf in ethanol makes it brittle – the water softens it	
Spread the leaf out on a white tile	So that the results are easy to see	
Add iodine solution to the leaf	To test for the presence of starch	Avoid skin contact with iodine solution

Factors needed for photosynthesis

Experiments can be used to find out what factors are needed for photosynthesis.

First, the plant is destarched. This involves leaving the plant in the dark for 48 hours. The plant uses up all the stores of starch in its leaves. One plant (or leaf) is exposed to all the conditions needed – this is the **control**. Another plant (or leaf) is deprived of one condition (this may be light, or carbon dioxide).

After a few hours the starch test is carried out on the control and test plant/leaf. The equation for photosynthesis shows the raw materials that a plant needs to make its food. Some plants have variegated leaves – only some parts of each leaf contain chlorophyll. When tested for starch, only the parts of the leaf with chlorophyll will contain starch.

The carbon dioxide around a plant can be controlled by keeping the plant in a sealed container with a carbon dioxide absorber such as sodium hydroxide pellets. The control plant would be in an identical container, without the carbon dioxide absorber.

● **Try this**   The answers are given on **p. 140.**

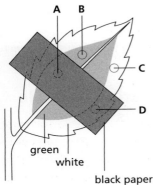

Figure 10.1

1 Figure 10.1 shows a variegated leaf in a photosynthesis experiment. Part of the leaf has been covered with black paper. The leaf was then exposed to light for a few hours. Leaf discs were then cut from regions of the leaf at **A, B, C** and **D**. Each disc was tested for the presence of starch.

Predict the results of the starch test on each region of the variegated leaf. Give a reason for each result.   [8 marks]

It is difficult to show that land plants produce oxygen during photosynthesis because the gas diffuses into the air. However, some aquatic plants produce bubbles of oxygen. These can be collected and tested with a glowing splint – this relights in oxygen.

● **Try this**   The answers are given on **p. 140.**

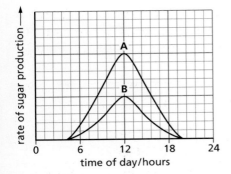

Figure 10.2

2 Figure 10.2 shows the rates of sugar production by a plant on a bright day and on a dull day.

a) i)   Which curve, **A** or **B**, shows sugar production on a bright day? State a reason for your choice.   [2 marks]
   ii) Outline the role of chloroplasts in photosynthesis.   [2 marks]
   iii) Suggest one feature of a leaf, other than the presence of chloroplasts, which might affect the amount of sugar produced.
                                                                     [1 mark]

b) i)   Suggest why many plants store starch rather than sugars. [1 mark]
   ii) Which chemical reagent is used to test for starch?   [1 mark]

Sample question and answer

Sample question   The chemical equation for photosynthesis shown below is incomplete.

$$6H_2O \text{ (water)} + \underline{\quad} \xrightarrow[\substack{\text{plant} \\ \text{pigment}}]{\text{energy}} C_6H_{12}O_6 \text{ (glucose)} + \underline{\quad}$$

i)   Complete the equation in either all words or all symbols.
                                                                     [2 marks]

ii) State the source of energy for this reaction.   [1 mark]

iii) Name the plant pigment necessary for this reaction.   [1 mark]

Student's answer   i) $6H_2O \text{ (water)} + 6CO_2$ ✓ $\xrightarrow[\text{plant pigment}]{\text{energy}} C_6H_{12}O_6 \text{ (glucose)} + \text{oxygen}$ ✗

ii) the sun ✗

iii) chloroplast ✗

continued

Examiner's comments

i) *Although the candidate has identified both compounds missing from the equation, she has written one in symbols and the second in words, so the examiner has not awarded the second mark. When you write an equation or complete one, always do it with either words or symbols — don't mix them up.*

ii) *'The sun' has not been accepted because this answer is not specific enough — the sun produces two types of energy (light and heat). Plants only use light energy in photosynthesis. The correct answer was light, or sunlight.*

iii) *Chloroplasts are structures, not pigments. They contain the pigment. Chlorophyll was the correct answer.*

Effects of light intensity and carbon dioxide concentration on photosynthesis

As light intensity increases, so does the rate of photosynthesis. This can be demonstrated as shown in Figure 10.3 (left-hand side), using an aquatic plant such as *Elodea*.

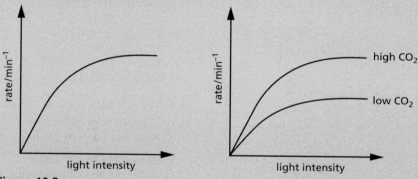

Figure 10.3

The light intensity (I) is related to the distance (d) between the lamp and the plant ($I = 1/d^2$). As the lamp is moved closer, the light intensity increases. The rate of photosynthesis is directly proportional to the light intensity, as shown by the left-hand graph in Figure 10.3. However, the photosynthetic rate cannot be increased indefinitely: a point is reached where all the chloroplasts cannot trap any more light.

Also, if there is a limiting factor (such as carbon dioxide) the rate of photosynthesis becomes limited, as shown in the right-hand graph.

Use of carbon dioxide enrichment, optimum light and optimum temperatures in greenhouse systems

Greenhouses are used in some countries to control conditions for plant growth, especially when growing conditions outside are not ideal. The glass helps trap heat inside, and atmospheric conditions can be controlled.

Carbon dioxide enrichment

Atmospheric air contains only 0.04% carbon dioxide, so it can easily become a factor that limits the rate of photosynthesis. A greenhouse is a closed system, so the content of the air in it can be controlled. For example, the amount of carbon dioxide can be increased by burning fossil fuels in the greenhouse, or releasing pure carbon dioxide from a gas cylinder.

Optimum light   If light conditions in a greenhouse are not optimum (e.g. in winter), they can be improved by using artificial lights.

● **Try this**   The answers are given on **p. 140**.

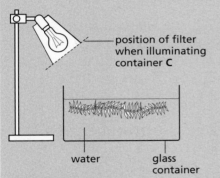

position of filter when illuminating container **C**

water   glass container

Figure 10.4

3   A student carried out an experiment to investigate the growth of floating water plants taken from a pond. Equal masses of the plants were placed into three separate glass containers **A**, **B** and **C**, similar to those shown in Figure 10.4.

Container **A** was lit by a 250 W bulb, **B** was lit by a 75 W bulb and **C** was lit by a 250 W bulb with a coloured filter in front of the lamp, as shown in the figure. At weekly intervals the plants were removed from each container in turn, gently dried, weighed, and returned to the containers after their mass had been recorded. Figure 10.5 shows the results.

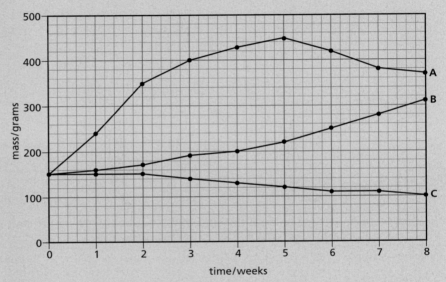

Figure 10.5

a) Calculate the percentage increase in mass of the plants in container **A** during the first five weeks of the experiment. (Show your working.)
[2 marks]

b) Suggest why the mass of plants in container **A** began to decrease after week 5, while the mass of plants in **B** continued to increase. [2 marks]

c) During the eighth week, in which container would there be the least dissolved oxygen? Explain your answer.   [2 marks]

Figure 10.6 shows the amount of light of different colours absorbed by chlorophyll. The filter used in illuminating container **C** allowed only one colour of light to pass through to the water plants.

d) Suggest which colour of light passed through the filter. Explain your answer.   [2 marks]

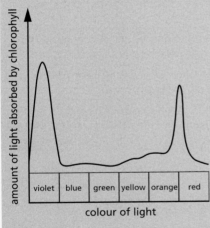

Figure 10.6

Optimum temperature   If the temperature is a limiting factor, e.g. in winter, it can be raised by using a heating system. If fossil fuels are burned, there is also a benefit from the carbon dioxide produced.

Leaf structure

You need to be able to identify the cellular and tissue structure of a leaf and relate the features to their functions.

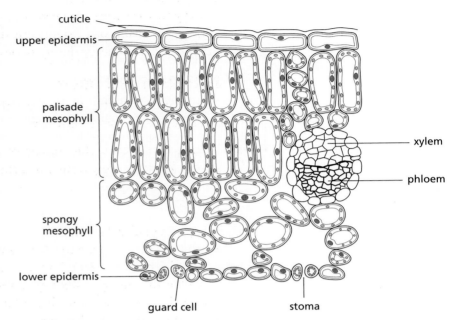

Figure 10.7 A cross-section through part of a leaf

Part of leaf	Details
Cuticle	Made of wax, waterproofing the leaf. It is secreted by cells of the upper epidermis
Upper epidermis	These cells are thin and transparent to allow light to pass through. No chloroplasts are present. They act as a barrier to disease organisms
Palisade mesophyll	Main region for photosynthesis. Cells are columnar (quite long) and packed with chloroplasts to trap light energy. They receive carbon dioxide by diffusion from air spaces in the spongy mesophyll
Spongy mesophyll	Cells are more spherical and loosely packed. They contain chloroplasts, but not as many as in palisade cells. Air spaces between cells allow gaseous exchange – carbon dioxide to the cells, oxygen from the cells during photosynthesis
Vascular bundle	This is a leaf vein, made up of **xylem** and **phloem**. Xylem vessels bring water and minerals to the leaf. Phloem vessels transport sugars and amino acids away (this is called translocation)
Lower epidermis	Acts as a protective layer. Stomata are present to regulate the loss of water vapour (this is called transpiration). Site of gaseous exchange into and out of the leaf
Stomata	Each stoma is surrounded by a pair of guard cells. These can control whether the stoma is open or closed. Water vapour passes out during transpiration. Carbon dioxide diffuses in and oxygen diffuses out during photosynthesis

● **Try this**   The answers are given on **p. 140**.

4 Copy, e.g. by tracing, the diagram of a leaf in Figure 10.7. Practise labelling the structures present. Annotate the diagram by writing one statement about each of the labels.

Importance of nitrate and magnesium ions

Nitrate ions are needed to synthesise (build up) proteins. Remember that all proteins contain the element nitrogen (see Topic 9). To build proteins, plants first make amino acids. Each amino acid is formed by combining sugars, made during photosynthesis, with nitrate. The amino acids are made into long chains by bonding them together. The proteins are used to make cytoplasm and enzymes.

Magnesium ions are needed to make chlorophyll. Each chlorophyll molecule contains one magnesium atom. Plants need chlorophyll to trap light to provide energy during photosynthesis.

Nitrogen fertilisers

You need to be able to describe the uses, and the dangers of overuse, of nitrogen fertilisers.

Uses   To increase crop yields. Intensive farming (repeatedly using the same land for crops) removes nitrates from the soil. These need to be replaced to prevent a drop in yield. Nitrates can be replaced in three ways:

- applying animal manure
- crop rotation – growing leguminous plants such as peas, beans and clover every 2 or 3 years: these plants develop root nodules containing nitrogen-fixing bacteria, and the roots are ploughed into the soil, boosting nitrate levels
- adding artificial fertilisers such as ammonium nitrate.

Dangers of overuse
- Wilting and death of plants. Applying too much nitrogen fertiliser can result in water being drawn out of the plant roots by osmosis. The plants wilt and may die.
- Eutrophication – this is the destruction of life in nearby rivers or lakes. The flowchart below shows the process.

Leaching
Nitrates are soluble – they can be leached out of the soil by heavy rainfall and are carried into the nearest water system such as a river
↓
Rapid algal growth
The presence of extra nitrates promotes growth of water plants (algae)
↓
Death of algae
Surface algal growth blocks light for algae below – as the surface algae grow more quickly, they also die
↓
Decay by bacteria
As the algae die, they are decomposed by bacteria – the bacteria respire aerobically, using up oxygen
↓
Death of aquatic animals
Fish and other aquatic animals die from lack of oxygen

Effects of nitrate ion and magnesium ion deficiencies on plant growth

Nitrate ion deficiency

You already know the importance of nitrate ions for protein synthesis. If the plant has a nitrate ion deficiency it will not be able to make proteins, so growth will slow down. The stem becomes weak, lower leaves become yellow and die, while upper leaves turn pale green.

Magnesium ion deficiency

You already know the importance of magnesium ions for synthesis of chlorophyll. If the plant has a magnesium ion deficiency it will not be able to make chlorophyll. Leaves turn yellow from the bottom of the stem upwards. Plant growth will suffer because it will have reduced photosynthesis. Yellowing of leaves due to lack of magnesium ions is called chlorosis.

● **Try this**   The answers are given on **p. 140**.

5 a) i) Plants need a supply of nitrate ions. State the use made of nitrate ions in plants.   [1 mark]

  ii) Many farmers regularly add nitrate fertilisers to their fields. Explain why this is necessary.   [2 marks]

  b) A farmer spreads a nitrate-rich fertiliser over his fields. Each time he does this, he washes out his spreading equipment in a farm pond. Suggest and explain what the likely effects of such pollution will be on the plants and animals in the pond.   [5 marks]

TOPIC 11 Human diet

- To be able to understand the concept of a *balanced diet*
- To be able to describe a balanced diet related to the age, sex and activity of an individual
- To be able to describe the effects of *malnutrition*
- To be able to describe the effects of alcohol and the dangers of its misuse
- To be able to discuss the problems of world food supplies
- To be able to discuss the problems that contribute to famine

Key definitions

Balanced diet	A diet that contains all the main nutrients in the correct amounts and proportions
Malnutrition	This is the result of not eating a balanced diet. There may be too little food or too much, or the diet could be lacking in one or more key nutrients

Key ideas

Balanced diet

This must contain all the essential nutrients in the correct proportions to maintain good health. The nutrients needed are carbohydrate, fat, protein, vitamins, minerals, fibre and water (see Topic 9 for further details).

● Try this

The answer is given on **p. 140**.

1 Make a mnemonic to remember all the nutrients in a balanced diet. You need to use the letters **C, F, P, V, M, F, W**.

An unbalanced diet could lead to a deficiency disease (see Topic 9) or to a disorder such as obesity.

Your dietary requirements depend on your age, sex and activity. The amount of energy needed is provided mainly by our carbohydrate and fat intake. Generally, males use up more energy than females, and the energy demand increases until we stop growing. Someone doing physical work will use up more energy than an office worker. While children are growing they need more protein per kilogram of body weight than adults do. Pregnant women need extra nutrients for the development of the fetus.

Effects of malnutrition

Malnutrition is the result of an unbalanced diet.

- Too much food, or too much carbohydrate, fat or protein can lead to obesity. This can lead to coronary heart disease and diabetes (which can cause blindness).

- Too much animal fat in the diet results in high cholesterol levels. Cholesterol can stick to the walls of arteries, gradually blocking them. If coronary arteries become blocked, the result can be angina and coronary heart disease.
- Too little food can result in starvation. Extreme slimming diets, such as those that avoid carbohydrate foods, can result in the disease anorexia nervosa.
- Sometimes the balance of food is wrong, e.g. too much carbohydrate and too little protein, such as when the bulk of the diet is starchy food, such as yam or cassava. This can lead to kwashiorkor in young children. They lack protein, but other problems such as plant toxins can also play a role.
- Constipation is caused by lack of fibre in the diet. It can lead to bowel cancer.
- Vitamin and mineral deficiency diseases are all the result of malnutrition (see Topic 9).

Sample question and answer

Sample question The chart is used to find a person's ideal mass.

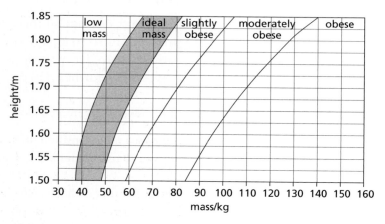

Figure 11.1

The following data were collected for three students: X, Y and Z.

Student	Mass/kg	Height/m
X	50.8	1.55
Y	63.8	1.85
Z	114.3	1.65

Identify the student who is:
i) obese
ii) of low mass
iii) of ideal mass.

[3 marks]

Student's answer
i) Z ✓
ii) X ✗
iii) Y ✗

This candidate has not used the chart to work out the student with low mass and ideal mass — the answer has been derived only from the table of data. Using only this table, student X appears to have low mass, but his height also needs to be taken into consideration (hence the need to use the chart).

Effects of alcohol and dangers of misuse

Alcohol is a drug — it affects the nervous system. Small amounts create a feeling of relaxation, but larger amounts affect balance and cause dizziness, slurred speech and problems with vision. Alcohol is a depressant. It affects judgement and slows down reaction time. Large amounts can result in unconsciousness. Long-term effects include addiction (alcoholism), cirrhosis of the liver, stomach ulcers, cancers of the digestive system and heart disease. Drinking during pregnancy can affect the fetus — increasing the risk of miscarriage and decreasing the average birth weight.

The problems of world food supplies and the causes of famine

There is not always enough food available in a country to feed the people living there. A severe food shortage can lead to famine. Food may have to be brought in (imported). Fresh food can have a limited storage life, so it needs to be transported quickly or treated to prevent it going rotten. Methods to increase the life of food include transport in chilled containers, or picking the produce before it is ripe. When it has reached its destination, it is exposed to chemicals such as plant auxins to bring on the ripening process. The use of aeroplanes to transport food is very expensive. The re-distribution of surplus food from first world countries to a poorer one can have a detrimental effect on that country's local economy by reducing the value of food grown by local farmers. Some food grown by countries with large debts may be exported as cash crops, even though local people desperately need the food. Other problems that can result in famine include:

- climate change and natural disasters such as flooding or drought
- pollution
- shortage of water through its use for other purposes, the diversion of rivers, building dams to provide hydroelectricity
- eating next year's seeds through desperation for food
- poor soil, lack of inorganic ions or fertiliser
- desertification due to soil erosion, as a result of deforestation
- lack of money to buy seeds, fertiliser, pesticides or machinery
- war, which can make it too dangerous to farm, or which removes labour
- urbanisation (building on farm land)
- an increasing population
- pest damage or disease
- poor education of farmers and outmoded farm practices
- the destruction of forests, so there is nothing to hunt and no food to collect.

TOPIC 12 Digestion and absorption

Key objectives

- To be able to identify the gross structure of the alimentary canal and describe the functions of its main organs
- To be able to define *ingestion*, *digestion*, *absorption*, *assimilation* and *egestion*
- To be able to identify the types of human teeth and describe their functions
- To be able to state the causes of dental decay and describe the proper care of teeth
- To be able to describe the processes of chewing and peristalsis
- To be able to describe digestion in the alimentary canal
- To be able to state the functions of key enzymes, listing substrates and end products
- To be able to identify the small intestine as the region for absorption of digested food
- To be able to describe the significance of villi in increasing the internal surface area
- To be able to describe the role of the liver regarding glucose and excess amino acids
- To be able to recall the role of fat as a storage compound
- To be able to explain the probable action of fluoride in reducing tooth decay
- To be able to present arguments for and against the addition of fluoride to public water supplies
- To be able to describe the structure of a villus and state the role of capillaries and lacteals
- To be able to state the role of the hepatic portal vein
- To be able to define *deamination*

Key definitions

Ingestion	Intake of food into the mouth
Digestion	The process of breaking down large, insoluble food molecules into smaller, soluble ones using enzymes
Absorption	The process of passing digested food molecules across the wall of the intestine into the blood or lymph
Assimilation	Uptake and use of food molecules by cells
Egestion	Passing out of undigested food, in the form of faeces, from the anus
Deamination	The removal of the nitrogen-containing part of amino acids as urea. (The remainder of the amino acid is used to supply energy)

Key ideas Gross structure and functions of parts of the alimentary canal

Figure 12.1 shows the main organs of the alimentary canal. The table below gives their functions.

Figure 12.1

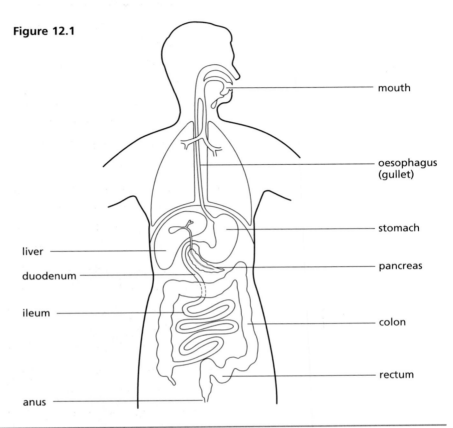

Organ	Function
Mouth	Food is ingested here. It is mechanically digested by cutting, chewing and grinding of teeth. Saliva is added – this contains amylase to begin the digestion of starch
Oesophagus	Boluses (balls) of food pass through by peristalsis, from mouth to stomach
Stomach	Muscular walls squeeze on food to make it semi-liquid. Gastric juice contains protease to digest protein and hydrochloric acid to maintain an optimum pH (1–2.5). The acid also kills bacteria
Duodenum	This is the first part of the small intestine. It receives pancreatic juice containing protease, lipase and amylase. The juice also contains sodium hydrogen carbonate, which neutralises acid from the stomach, producing a pH of 7–8
Pancreas	Secretes pancreatic juice into the duodenum. Also makes the hormones insulin and glucagon (see pages 46 and 79–80 on the liver)
Liver	Makes bile, which is stored in the gall bladder. Bile contains salts that emulsify fats, forming droplets with a large surface area to make digestion by lipase more efficient. Digested foods are assimilated here. For example, glucose is stored as glycogen; surplus amino acids are deaminated (see Topic 16)
Ileum	The second part of the small intestine. Enzymes in the epithelial lining break down maltose and peptides. Its surface area is increased by the presence of villi which allow the efficient absorption of digested food molecules
Colon	The second part of the large intestine. Its main function is the reabsorption of water from undigested food. It also absorbs bile salts to pass back to the liver
Rectum	This stores faeces until it is egested
Anus	This has muscles to control when faeces is egested from the body

Common misconceptions

The liver does not make digestive enzymes – bile is not an enzyme. It breaks fat down into smaller droplets, but does not change them chemically.

The fat molecules stay the same size; it is just the droplet size that changes from large to small due to the action of bile. ■

Human teeth

You only need to know about the types and functions of human teeth. It also helps to know about tooth structure, as this is important in describing the process of tooth decay. Figure 12.2 shows the types and functions of human teeth.

	Incisor	Canine	Premolar	Molar
Position in mouth	Front	Either side of incisors	Behind canines	Back
Description	Chisel-shaped (sharp edge)	Slightly more pointed than incisors	Have two points (cusps). Have one/two roots	Have four/five cusps. Have two/three roots
Function	Biting off pieces of food	Similar function to incisors	Tearing and grinding food	Chewing and grinding food

Figure 12.2

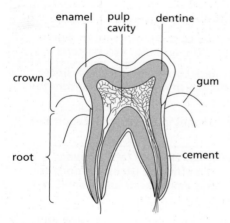

Figure 12.3

Structure of a tooth

Figure 12.3 shows a section through a molar tooth.

Causes of dental decay

Bacteria are present on the surface of our teeth. Food deposits and bacteria form a layer called plaque. Bacteria in the plaque feed on sugars, producing acid. This acid dissolves enamel, forming a hole.

Dentine underneath the enamel is softer – it dissolves more rapidly.

If the hole reaches the pulp cavity, bacterial infection can get to the nerve. This results in toothache and, possibly, an abscess (an infection in the jaw).

Common misconceptions

Do not say that sugar causes tooth decay. It only causes problems because of the activity of bacteria feeding on it and producing acids. ■

● **Try this** The answers are given on **p. 140**.

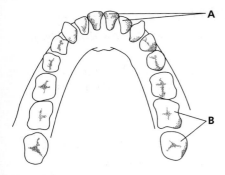

Figure 12.4

1 Figure 12.4 shows the four types of teeth found in humans.

a) Copy the figure and name on it **one** example of each of the four types of teeth.

[4 marks]

b) i)   What is the function of the teeth labelled **A**?   [1 mark]
   ii) What is the function of the teeth labelled **B**?   [1 mark]

c) The outer layer of the crown of a tooth is resistant to attack by bacteria.
   i)   Name this outer layer.   [1 mark]
   ii)   State the mineral and the vitamin needed in the diet for the healthy development of this layer.   [2 marks]
   iii) Explain how bacteria can gain entry through this layer into the tooth and cause dental decay.   [3 marks]

Proper care of teeth

- Avoid sugary food, especially between meals, so bacteria cannot make acid and clean teeth regularly to remove plaque.
- Use dental floss or a toothpick to remove pieces of food and plaque trapped between teeth.
- Use a fluoride toothpaste (or drink fluoridated water) – fluoride hardens tooth enamel.
- Visit a dentist regularly to make sure any tooth decay is treated early and any stubborn plaque (called calculus) is removed.

Fluoride

You need to be able to explain the action of fluoride in reducing tooth decay, and to present arguments for and against its addition to public water supplies.

Growing children can absorb fluoride in their diet (from toothpaste or fluoridated water). It becomes part of the enamel of their developing teeth, and the enamel is then more resistant to tooth decay.

Adding fluoride to public water supplies

Arguments for:
- Tooth decay in the local population of children decreases.
- There is no need to buy fluoridated toothpaste.

Arguments against:
- It is a form of mass medication – people have no choice about whether or not they want the treatment.
- Fluoride can cause mottling of the teeth – white patches (fluorosis).
- Fluoride is a benefit only to growing children – adults do not benefit.
- If people take proper care of their teeth, fluoridation is unnecessary.
- Fluoride may have side effects, such as an increase in risk of bone cancer (but this is unlikely).

There is a big difference between fluoride and fluorine. Fluorine is a very toxic gas, while fluoride is a mineral that helps to strengthen teeth. Make sure you do not use the term *fluorine* in an exam answer about teeth! ■

Chewing and peristalsis

Chewing is a form of mechanical digestion. It is performed by the teeth, and results in pieces of food being mixed with saliva and becoming smaller. The smaller pieces are easier to swallow and have a larger surface area.

Peristalsis is the way food is moved along the alimentary canal. The canal, from oesophagus to rectum, has a layer of circular muscle. The muscle contracts behind the food and relaxes in front of it, allowing the food to be pushed forward.

Digestion in the alimentary canal

Food that we ingest is mainly made up of large, insoluble molecules that cannot be absorbed through the gut wall. It needs to be changed into small, soluble molecules.

Physical digestion involves breaking large pieces of food into smaller pieces. This increases the surface area of the food, and is achieved by chewing food in the mouth and churning food in the stomach and intestine. Bile physically digests fats by emulsifying them – turning them into small droplets with a large surface area.

Chemical digestion involves breaking down large, insoluble molecules into small, soluble ones. Enzymes speed up the process. They work efficiently at body temperature (37°C) and at a suitable pH. The main places where chemical digestion happens are the mouth, stomach and small intestine.

You need to be able to state the functions of amylase, protease and lipase.

Enzyme	Site of action	Special conditions	Substrate digested	End product(s)
Amylase	Mouth, duodenum	Slightly alkaline	Starch	Maltose, glucose
Protease	Stomach, duodenum	Acid in stomach, alkaline in duodenum	Protein	Amino acids
Lipase	Duodenum	Alkaline	Fat	Fatty acids and glycerol

The liver and pancreas are important in secreting juices (bile and pancreatic juice) to aid digestion (see the table on page 41).

Chewing food does not involve breaking down large molecules into small molecules; it only breaks down large pieces into smaller pieces, giving a larger surface area for enzymes to work on. ■

Function of the small intestine and significance of villi

You need to be able to relate the structure of the small intestine to its function of absorbing digested food and describe the significance of villi in increasing the internal surface area.

The **small intestine** has a very rich blood supply. Digested food molecules are small enough to pass through the wall of the intestine into the bloodstream.

Villi are present – these are finger-like projections that increase the surface area for absorption. If a section of small intestine was turned inside out, its surface would be like a carpet.

Inside each **villus** are blood capillaries that absorb amino acids and glucose. There are also **lacteals** – these absorb fatty acids and glycerol.

Food molecules are absorbed mainly by diffusion. Figure 12.5 shows the features of a villus that increase the efficiency of diffusion. Molecules can also be absorbed by active transport.

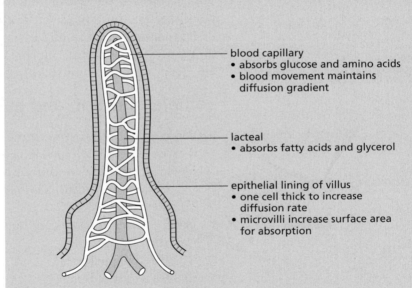

blood capillary
- absorbs glucose and amino acids
- blood movement maintains diffusion gradient

lacteal
- absorbs fatty acids and glycerol

epithelial lining of villus
- one cell thick to increase diffusion rate
- microvilli increase surface area for absorption

Figure 12.5

Examiner's tips
▶ Absorption in the small intestine involves diffusion and active transport (described in Topic 6). Check that you can relate how the structure of a villus makes these processes efficient.

Epithelial cells contain mitochondria to provide energy for absorption against the concentration gradient.

Role of the hepatic portal vein

You need to be able to describe the role of the hepatic portal vein in the transport of absorbed food to the liver.

The hepatic portal vein transports absorbed food from the small intestine to the liver. After a meal, the blood in this vein contains very high concentrations of glucose and amino acids, as well as vitamins and minerals. The liver reduces levels back to normal.

Role of the liver

You need to be able to describe the role of the liver regarding glucose and excess amino acids.

Excess glucose in the blood arriving at the liver is converted into glycogen (animal starch) for storage, or broken down through respiration, producing energy for other purposes.

Excess amino acids cannot be stored in the body. The liver removes these from the blood and breaks them down forming urea and an energy source.

Role of fat

You need to be able to describe the role of fat as a storage compound.

Fatty acids and glycerol, absorbed into the lymphatic system through the lacteals in villi, are carried in lymph to the bloodstream. Body cells take up the re-formed fat molecules. They may be used in respiration as a source of energy, or stored. Fat is a good storage compound – it releases twice as much energy as carbohydrates when respired, and acts as insulation in the skin. Some nerve cells form a myelin sheath from fat, to prevent electrical impulses from leaking out.

Sample question and answer

Sample question

a) Proteins are digested in the stomach and small intestine.
  i) Which type of enzyme breaks down proteins?   [1 mark]
  ii) State how the conditions necessary for the digestion of proteins in the stomach are different from those in the small intestine.   [1 mark]
b) When carbohydrates have been digested, excess glucose is stored.
  i) Where is it stored?   [1 mark]
  ii) What is it stored as?   [1 mark]
c) Excess amino acids cannot be stored. Describe how they are removed from the body.   [4 marks]

Student's answer

a) i) protease ✓
  ii) It is acid in the stomach and alkaline in the small intestine. ✓
b) i) in the liver ✓
  ii) glucagon ✗
c) The liver ✓ breaks them down. This makes urea ✓.
  The kidney filters out the urea. ✓

Examiner's comments

Answers to parts (a) and (b) are good, except that the candidate has got glucagon (a hormone) mixed up with glycogen (the correct answer). Names like this have to be accurately spelt. The answer for part (c) contains only three statements. Further details about the filtering of blood or the formation of urine and its removal by urination would have achieved the final mark.

TOPIC 13 Transport in plants

Key objectives

- To be able to identify root hair cells, as seen under the light microscope, and describe their functions
- To be able to describe the passage of water through root, stem and leaf
- To be able to define *transpiration*
- To be able to describe how water vapour loss is related to cell surfaces, air spaces and stomata
- To be able to describe the factors affecting transpiration rate
- To be able to describe how wilting occurs
- To be able to define *translocation*
- To be able to describe the mechanisms of water uptake and water movement through a plant
- To be able to describe the adaptations of the leaf, stem and root to different environments
- To be able to describe the translocation of applied chemicals, including systemic pesticides

Key definitions

Transpiration	Loss of water vapour from the leaves through the stomata by **diffusion**
Translocation	Movement of sucrose and amino acids from regions of production or of storage to regions of use for respiration or growth

Key ideas

Root hair cells

These form on young roots to increase the surface area of the root for absorption of water and mineral ions, as well as providing anchorage for the plant. Figure 13.1 shows a root hair cell.

The cell extension (the hair) increases the surface area of the cell to make it more efficient in absorbing materials.

● Try this

The answers are given on **p. 140.**

1 a) Copy or trace the root hair cell in Figure 13.1. Label all its parts; remembering to use a ruler for all label lines. [5 marks]
   b) Which plant cell part is missing from this cell? [1 mark]
   c) Name the process by which the cell absorbs:
      i) water [1 mark]
      ii) mineral ions. [1 mark]

Figure 13.1

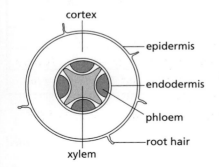

Figure 13.2

Passage of water through root, stem and leaf

Water passes through the cells of the root by osmosis, reaching the xylem vessels in the centre. Figure 13.2 shows a section through a root.

When water reaches the xylem it travels up these vessels, through the stem to the leaves. Mature xylem cells have no cell contents, so they act like open-ended tubes allowing free movement of water through them. In the leaves, water passes out of the xylem vessels into the surrounding cells. Mineral ions are also transported through the xylem.

Transpiration is the loss of water vapour from a leaf. Water in the leaf cells forms a thin layer on their surfaces. The water evaporates into the air spaces in the spongy mesophyll. This creates a high concentration of water molecules. They diffuse out of the leaf into the surrounding air, through the stomata, by diffusion.

Factors affecting transpiration rate

The table shows the factors that can result in an increase in the rate of transpiration. If these factors are reversed, the rate will decrease.

Factor	Explanation
Increase in temperature	Increases the kinetic (movement) energy of water molecules, so they diffuse faster
Increase in air movement, e.g. wind	Removes water molecules as they pass out of the leaf, maintaining a steep concentration gradient for diffusion
Decrease in humidity	Results in a lower concentration of water molecules outside the leaf, making a steeper concentration gradient for diffusion
Increase in light intensity	Stomata open to allow gas exchange for photosynthesis, so water vapour can diffuse out of the leaf

Examiner's tip
▶ Most of the factors that result in a change in transpiration rate are linked to diffusion. When writing explanations, try to include references to the concentration gradient caused by a change in the factor.

● **Try this**   The answers are given on **p. 140**.

2 Figure 13.3 shows part of the lower surface of a typical dicotyledonous leaf.

a) On the figure, label part **A** and the cells **B** and **C**.   [3 marks]

The surfaces of the leaves of two species of plant were studied and the number of stomata per unit area (stomatal frequency) was recorded.
  Cobalt chloride paper changes colour in the presence of water.
  Pieces of cobalt chloride paper were attached to the upper and lower surfaces of leaves on both plants. The plants were set up for one hour during the day. Any colour changes were recorded. The experiment was repeated for one hour at night. The table shows the results.

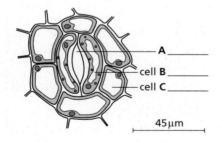

A _____
cell B _____
cell C _____

45 μm

Figure 13.3

Plant species	Stomatal frequency		Colour change to cobalt chloride paper			
	Lower surface	Upper surface	Day		Night	
			Lower surface	Upper surface	Lower surface	Upper surface
Cassia fistula	0	18	✗	✓	✗	✗
Bauhinia monandra	22	0	✓	✗	✗	✗
Key: ✓ colour change; ✗ no colour change.						

continued

b) Describe the differences in stomatal distribution between the two species of plant. [2 marks]

c) **i)** Explain the colour changes to the cobalt chloride paper during the day. [3 marks]

   ii) Suggest why there was no colour change for either plant at night. [1 mark]

d) Outline the mechanism by which water in the roots reaches the leaf. [3 marks]

e) State and explain the effect of the following on transpiration rate:

   i) increasing humidity [2 marks]

   ii) increasing temperature. [2 marks]

How wilting occurs

Young plant stems and leaves rely on their cells being turgid to keep them rigid. If the amount of water lost from the leaves of a plant is greater than the amount taken into the roots, the plant will have a water shortage. Cells become flaccid if they lack water, and they will no longer press against each other. Stems and leaves then lose their rigidity, and wilt.

Mechanism of water uptake

Water enters root hair cells by osmosis. This happens when the water potential in the soil surrounding the root is higher than in the cell. As the water enters the cell, its water potential becomes higher than in the cell next to it, e.g. in the cortex. So the water moves, by osmosis, into the next cell. The process is repeated until water reaches the xylem. Water also passes from cell to cell along the cell walls.

Mechanism of water movement through a plant

Water vapour evaporating from a leaf creates a kind of suction, as water molecules are attracted to each other. So more water is drawn into the leaf from the xylem. This creates a transpiration stream, pulling water up from the root. Xylem vessels act like tiny tubes – drawing water up the stem by capillary action. Roots also produce a root pressure, forcing water up xylem vessels.

Refer back to Topic 5 to remind yourself of the structure of xylem tissue.

Common misconceptions

Water does not travel through xylem vessels by osmosis. Remember that osmosis involves the movement of water across cell membranes – xylem cells do not have living contents when mature, so there will be no membranes. ■

Sample question and answer

Sample question   **i)** Describe how the structure of xylem tissue is adapted to its functions.   [3 marks]

ii) Describe the mechanism of water movement through the xylem.   [2 marks]

Student's answer   **i)** The cells join together to make a long ✓ tubular structure. There are no cross-walls ✓ and no living contents ✓ so the water and mineral salts (✓) can pass through freely.

ii) Water moves by the pull from the leaves ✓ caused by transpiration. ✓ Xylem vessels are very thin, so they act like a capillary tube (✓) helping to draw water upwards.

Examiner's comments   *Both answers are excellent, gaining the maximum marks available. This candidate has learned the details of water transport in plants really well. The ticks in brackets mean that the statements are correct, but the maximum for the question has already been reached.*

Adaptations of leaf, stem and root to different environments

Where possible, you should be able to describe these features based on plants you are familiar with and that grow in your local area.

Most modifications are adaptations to very dry (arid) environments. Plants modified to cope with a lack of water are called **xerophytes**.

Plant	Modifications
Ammophila (marram grass)	• Very long roots to search for water deep down in sand dunes • Leaves that roll up in dry weather to increase humidity around stomata, reducing transpiration • Sunken stomata to create high humidity and reduce transpiration • Fine hairs around stomata, reducing air movement so humidity builds up and transpiration is reduced
Opuntia (prickly pear cactus)	• Leaves reduced to spines – this reduces the surface area for transpiration and also acts as a defence against herbivores • Reduced number of stomata • Stomata closed during the day – when conditions for transpiration are most favourable • Fleshy stem – to store water
Pinus (pine tree)	• Leaves needle-shaped to reduce surface area for transpiration and to resist wind damage • Sunken stomata to create high humidity and reduce transpiration • Thick waxy cuticle on the epidermis to prevent evaporation from leaf surface

Translocation of applied chemicals

You need to be able to describe the translocation of applied chemicals, including systemic pesticides.

Chemicals may be sprayed on to the leaves of a plant because they can be absorbed and enter the plant's transport system. Once in the leaf they are transported through the phloem to other parts of the plant by translocation. Systemic pesticides are applied this way. If an animal feeds on the plant while the pesticides are in the sap, it will take in the pesticide and become poisoned. In this way, insect pests such as caterpillars and aphids can be controlled, and crop yield is increased.

TOPIC 14 Transport in humans

Key objectives

- To be able to describe the gross structure and function of the heart
- To be able to describe the effect of exercise on heartbeat
- To be able to list the likely cause of a heart attack and preventive measures
- To be able to describe the structures and functions of arteries, veins and capillaries
- To be able to describe the double circulatory system
- To be able to identify blood cells
- To be able to describe the components and functions of the blood
- To be able to describe the transfer of materials between capillaries and tissue fluid
- To be able to describe the immune system
- To be able to describe the process of blood clotting
- To be able to describe the function of the lymphatic system

Key ideas

Structure and function of the heart

The heart is a pump, made of muscle, which moves blood around the body. The muscle is constantly active, so it needs its own blood supply, through the coronary artery, to provide it with oxygen and glucose.

The heart has two sides – the right side receives deoxygenated blood from the body and pumps it to the lungs for oxygenation, while the left side receives oxygenated blood from the lungs and pumps it to the body.

> **Examiner's tips**
> ▶ To remember which side of the heart contains oxygenated blood, learn this mnemonic: **LORD** (Left Oxygenated Right Deoxygenated).
> ▶ Arteries carry blood Away from the heart (remember AA).
> ▶ On a diagram, the right chambers are on the left of the diagram.

There are four chambers. The right and left atria receive blood from veins and squeeze it into the ventricles. The right and left ventricles receive blood from the atria and squeeze it into arteries. The wall of the left ventricle is much thicker than the right ventricle because it needs to build up enough pressure to move the blood to all the main organs. Figure 14.1 on the next page shows the main parts of the heart.

● Try this

The answer is given on **p. 141**.

1 Trace the heart in Figure 14.1 and draw arrows on the four blood vessels and the four chambers to show the direction of blood flow through the heart.

Shade the right chambers blue to show deoxygenated blood.

Shade the left chambers red to show oxygenated blood.

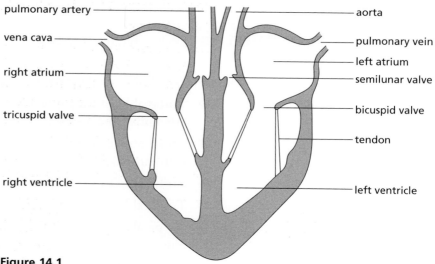

Figure 14.1

Common misconceptions

Remember that blood passing through the chambers of the heart does **not** supply the heart muscle with oxygen or glucose. The heart muscle has its own blood supply – via the coronary arteries – to do this. ■

Effect of exercise on heartbeat

A heartbeat is a contraction. Each contraction squeezes blood to the lungs and body. The heart beats about 70 times a minute, more if you are younger, and the rate becomes lower the fitter you are. During exercise the heart rate increases to supply the muscles with more oxygen and glucose. These are needed to allow the muscles to respire aerobically, so they have sufficient energy to contract. Regular exercise is important to keep the heart muscle in good tone. This results in the heart being more efficient in maintaining blood pressure and reduces the risk of coronary heart disease and stroke.

You need to be able to list the main causes of a heart attack and state preventive measures. The table outlines these.

Cause	Explanation	Preventive measures
Poor diet with too much saturated (animal) fat	Leads to cholesterol building up in arteries, eventually blocking the blood vessel or allowing a blood clot to form	Cholesterol-free diet
Smoking	Nicotine damages the heart and blood vessels (see Topic 15)	Stop smoking
Stress	Tends to increase blood pressure, which can result in fatty materials collecting in the arteries	Find ways of relaxing. Identify the causes of stress and avoid them
Obesity	Being overweight puts extra strain on the heart and makes it more difficult for the person to exercise	Go on a controlled diet and take regular exercise
Lack of exercise	The heart muscle loses its tone and becomes less efficient in pumping blood	Start taking regular exercise
Inherited factors	Heart disease appears to be passed from one generation to the next in some families	Make sure other factors do not increase the risk of heart disease. Monitor health

Structures and functions of arteries, veins and capillaries

Arteries carry blood at high pressure, away from the heart to organs of the body. **Veins** return blood, at low pressure, from organs towards the heart. **Capillaries** link arteries to veins. They carry blood through organs and tissues, allowing materials to be exchanged.

The table compares the structures of arteries, veins and capillaries. The explanation of how the structure is related to the function is only needed for the higher-tier paper – this work is part of the extended curriculum.

Blood vessel	Structure	How structure is related to function
Artery	Thick, tough wall with muscles, elastic fibres and fibrous tissue	Carries blood at high pressure – prevents bursting and maintains pressure wave
	Lumen quite narrow, but increases as a pulse of blood passes through	This helps to maintain blood pressure
	Valves absent	High pressure prevents blood flowing backwards
Vein	Thin wall – mainly fibrous tissue, with little muscle or elastic fibres	Carries blood at low pressure
	Lumen large	To reduce resistance to blood flow
	Valves present	To prevent backflow of blood
Capillary	Permeable wall, one cell thick, with no muscle or elastic tissue	Allows diffusion of materials between capillary and surrounding tissues
	Lumen approximately one red blood cell wide	White blood cells can squeeze between cells of the wall
	Valves absent	Blood cells pass through slowly to allow diffusion of materials and tissue fluid
		Blood pressure is lower than in arteries

The double circulatory system

Blood passes through the heart twice for each complete circulation of the body. The right side of the heart collects deoxygenated blood from the body and pumps it to the lungs. The left side collects oxygenated blood from the lungs and pumps it to the body. The double circulatory system helps to maintain blood pressure, making circulation efficient. Figure 14.2 shows the double circulatory system.

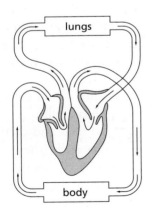

Figure 14.2

● **Try this**   The answers are given on **p. 141**.

2 **a)** On a copy of the diagram of the double circulatory system, label:
  i)   the four main blood vessels   [4 marks]
  ii) the chambers of the heart   [4 marks]
  iii) the two valves shown.   [2 marks]
  b) State two differences in composition between blood leaving the right ventricle and blood entering the left atrium.   [2 marks]

Sample question and answer

Sample question   Figure 14.3 shows a section through the heart.

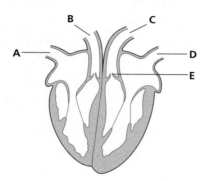

Figure 14.3

i)   Name the two blood vessels **A** and **B**.   [2 marks]
ii) Which of blood vessels **A**, **B**, **C** or **D** carry   [1 mark]
     oxygenated blood?
iii) Name valve **E** and state its function.   [3 marks]

Student's answer   i)   **A**, vena cava ✓ **B**, pulmonary vein ✗
ii) **C** ✗
iii) name: semilunar valve ✓ function: to stop
     blood going backwards ✓

Examiner's comments   *Blood vessel **B** is the pulmonary artery. Arteries of the heart always carry blood from a ventricle. Part ii) needs two answers (blood vessels **C** and **D**) to gain the mark. **D** is the pulmonary vein, which carries oxygenated blood to the heart from the lungs. **C** is the aorta, which carries oxygenated blood from the heart to the body. In part iii) the name of the valve is correct, but there are two marks for its function. This candidate has given only one statement: a second mark was available for stating that the valve prevents blood from going back into the left ventricle.*

Blood – cells and functions

You need to be able to recognise the main types of blood cells and describe the functions of the blood.

Blood is made up of a liquid (plasma) containing blood cells. Figure 14.4 on the facing page gives details of blood cells.

Plasma is a liquid that transports substances to cells and carries wastes away from cells. It acts as a pool for amino acids (these cannot be stored in the body) and contains blood proteins that are important in blood clotting. The table on the facing page shows the main substances carried by plasma.

Substance carried in plama	From	To
Amino acids	Small intestine	Sites of growth and repair
Carbon dioxide	Respiring tissues	Lungs
Glucose	Small intestine	All tissues
Heat	Liver, muscles	All tissues
Hormones, e.g. insulin	Endocrine glands, e.g. pancreas	Target organ, e.g. liver
Urea	Liver	Kidneys

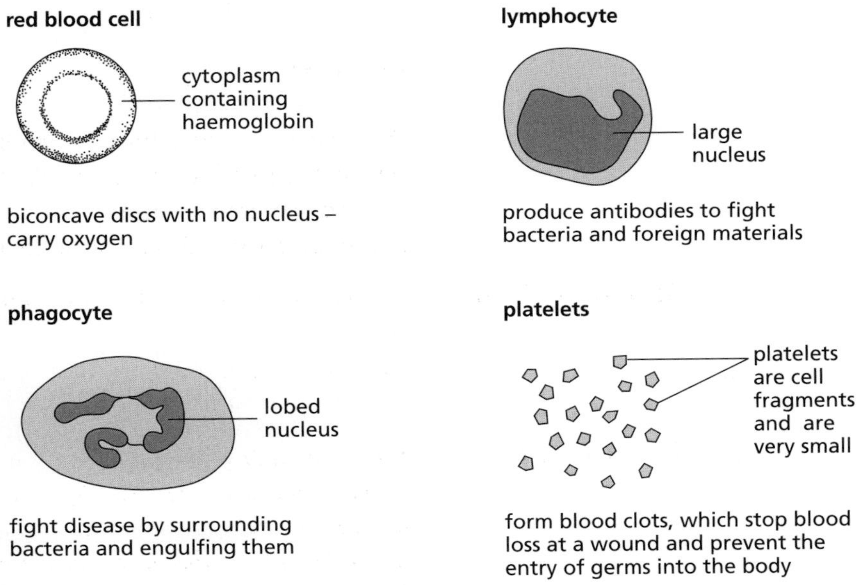

red blood cell

cytoplasm containing haemoglobin

biconcave discs with no nucleus – carry oxygen

lymphocyte

large nucleus

produce antibodies to fight bacteria and foreign materials

phagocyte

lobed nucleus

fight disease by surrounding bacteria and engulfing them

platelets

platelets are cell fragments and are very small

form blood clots, which stop blood loss at a wound and prevent the entry of germs into the body

Figure 14.4 Different types of blood cells

Transport of oxygen

Oxygen is not included in the table above, as it is transported in red blood cells. Oxygen combines with haemoglobin to form oxyhaemoglobin. The oxygen is released from the red blood cells in capillaries where surrounding oxygen levels are low.

Capillaries and tissues

You need to be able to describe the transfer of materials between capillaries and tissue fluid.

As blood enters capillaries from arterioles (small arteries), it slows down. This allows substances in the plasma, as well as oxygen from red blood cells, to diffuse through the capillary wall into the surrounding tissues (the capillary wall is thin and permeable). Liquid in the plasma also passes out. This forms tissue fluid, bathing the cells. Waste products from the cells, e.g. carbon dioxide, diffuse back through the capillary walls into the plasma. Some of the tissue fluid also passes back.

The immune system

You need to be able to describe the immune system in terms of antibody production, tissue rejection and phagocytosis.

The immune system is the body's defence against disease and foreign bodies. This defence takes the following forms.

- **Antibody production** – antibodies are produced by lymphocytes, which are formed in lymph nodes. Lymphocytes produce antibodies in response to the presence of pathogens such as bacteria. This is because alien cells have chemicals called antigens on their surface. A different antibody is produced for each antigen. The antibodies make bacteria clump together in preparation for action by phagocytes, or neutralise the toxins produced by the bacteria. Once antibodies have been made, they remain in the blood to provide long-term protection. Some lymphocytes memorise the antigens the body has been exposed to. They can rapidly reproduce and produce antibodies to respond to further infections by the same pathogen (disease-causing organism).
- **Tissue rejection** – transplants involve replacing a damaged organ with a donor organ. However, the body treats the replacement as an invading organism and this triggers an immune response. The donor organ is rejected as a result of the production of antibodies to fight the foreign tissue. To prevent this happening, the donor organ needs to be a similar tissue type to that of the patient, e.g. from a close relative. Immunosuppressive drugs are used, which switch off the body's immune response. While recovering, transplant patients are at risk of dying from any disease they are exposed to, so they need to be kept in isolation.
- **Phagocytosis** – phagocytes have the ability to move out of capillaries to the site of an infection. They then engulf (ingest) the infecting pathogens and kill them by digesting them.

Blood clotting

Blood plasma contains the soluble protein fibrinogen. If a blood vessel is damaged or if blood is exposed to air, fibrinogen is converted to insoluble fibrin. This forms threads, which trap red blood cells to make a blood clot.

The lymphatic system

The lymphatic system is a collection of lymph vessels and glands. It has three main roles.

- The return of tissue fluid to the blood in the form of **lymph fluid**. This prevents fluid build-up in the tissues.
- The production of **lymphocytes**. These are made in lymph glands such as the tonsils, adenoids and spleen. The glands become more active during an infection because they are producing and releasing large numbers of lymphocytes.
- The absorption of **fatty acids** and **glycerol** from the small intestine. Each villus contains a lacteal – a blind-ending lymph vessel.

TOPIC 15 Respiration

Key objectives

- To be able to define *respiration*, *aerobic respiration* and *anaerobic respiration*
- To be able to state the word equation for aerobic respiration
- To be able to name and describe the uses of energy in the human body
- To be able to state the word equations for anaerobic respiration in muscles and yeast
- To be able to compare aerobic and anaerobic respiration
- To be able to describe the production of lactic acid in muscles during exercise
- To be able to describe the role of anaerobic respiration in breadmaking and brewing
- To be able to list the features of gaseous exchange surfaces in animals
- To be able to state the differences in composition between inspired and expired air
- To be able to describe a test for carbon dioxide
- To be able to describe the effects of physical activity on rate and depth of breathing
- To be able to describe the effects of tobacco smoke on the respiratory system
- To be able to state the symbol equations for aerobic and anaerobic respiration
- To be able to describe the role of the ribs, intercostal muscles and diaphragm in ventilation of the lungs

Key definitions

Respiration	Release of energy from food substances in cells
Aerobic respiration	Breakdown of glucose in the presence of oxygen to release energy
Anaerobic respiration	Breakdown of glucose in the absence of oxygen to release energy`

Key ideas

Respiration

Respiration is a process carried out in cells (don't confuse it with breathing). For the Core curriculum, you need to be able to write the word equations for respiration. The symbol equations are part of the Extended curriculum. The energy formed during respiration is in the form of ATP (adenosine triphosphate).

Aerobic respiration:

glucose + oxygen $\rightarrow$ water + carbon dioxide + energy

$$C_6H_{12}O_6 + 6O_2 \rightarrow 6H_2O + 6CO_2 + \text{energy}$$

Anaerobic respiration in muscles:

glucose $\rightarrow$ lactic acid + energy

$$C_6H_{12}O_6 \rightarrow 2C_3H_6O_3 + \text{energy}$$

Anaerobic respiration in yeast:

glucose $\rightarrow$ ethanol + carbon dioxide + energy

$$C_6H_{12}O_6 \rightarrow 2C_2H_5OH + 2CO_2 + \text{energy}$$

Examiner's tips
▶ If you write a symbol equation, you must make sure the formulae are correct and that the equation is balanced.
▶ Anaerobic respiration in muscles does **not** produce carbon dioxide or water.
▶ Anaerobic respiration in yeast does **not** produce water.

In humans, energy is usually released by **aerobic respiration** – this is most efficient, producing 38 molecules of ATP (energy storage molecules) for each molecule of glucose broken down. However, the cells must receive plenty of oxygen to maintain this process.

Anaerobic respiration produces only 2 molecules of ATP. The energy released through respiration is used in the body for movement, maintaining a constant body temperature and building molecules.

Muscles respire anaerobically when exercising vigorously, because the blood cannot supply enough oxygen to maintain aerobic respiration. However, the formation and build-up of lactic acid in muscles causes cramp (muscle fatigue). An oxygen debt is created because oxygen is needed to convert lactic acid back to a harmless chemical (pyruvic acid). At the end of a race, a sprinter has to pant to get sufficient oxygen to the muscles to repay the oxygen debt. A long-distance runner has to pace herself to prevent her muscles respiring anaerobically. Muscle cramp would stop the athlete running.

Yeast is used in breadmaking and brewing, because of the products produced when it respires.

Breadmaking – yeast is mixed with water and sugar to activate it. The mixture is added to flour to make dough. This is left in a warm place to rise. The dough rises because the yeast is releasing carbon dioxide, which gets trapped in the dough. A warm temperature is important because respiration is controlled by enzymes (see Topic 8). When the dough is cooked, the high temperature kills the yeast and any ethanol formed evaporates. Air spaces are left where the carbon dioxide was trapped. This gives the bread a light texture.

Brewing – yeast is added to a source of sugar (this may be in fruit juice or in germinated barley grains) and kept in warm conditions. As the yeast respires the sugar – a process called fermentation – ethanol is formed, making the drink alcoholic. The fermenting mixture needs to be kept germ-free to prevent fungi or bacteria converting ethanol to ethanoic acid (vinegar). Carbon dioxide makes the drink fizzy and gives it a slightly sharp flavour, due to its acidity when dissolved in water.

Gaseous exchange

This process involves the passage of gases such as oxygen into, and carbon dioxide out of, cells or a transport system.

First, air needs to be in contact with the gaseous exchange surface. This is achieved by breathing. Figure 15.1 shows the breathing system of a human.

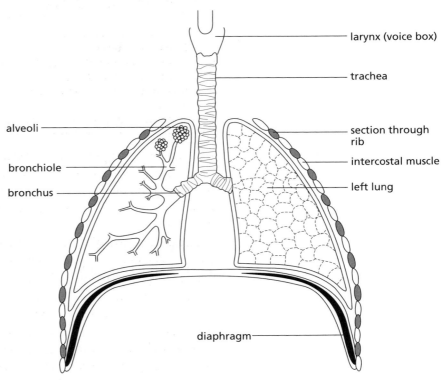

Figure 15.1

Examiner's tip

▶ To remember the sequence of structures through which air passes when you breathe in, imagine an apple tree:

Trunk	**Trachea**
Bough	**Bronchus**
Branch	**Bronchiole**
Apples	**Alveoli**

Gaseous exchange relies on diffusion. To be efficient, the gaseous exchange surface must:

- be **thin** – a short distance for gases to diffuse
- be **moist** – to allow gases to dissolve
- have a **large surface area** – for gases to diffuse over
- have a **concentration gradient** maintained across the surface – achieved by the movement or air (ventilation) and the transport or use of the gas.

These features are present in gills and lungs. Small invertebrates, such as earthworms, take in oxygen over their skin surface. They need to have a large surface area to obtain sufficient oxygen, and their skin is thin and moist.

Examples of gaseous exchange surfaces are the alveoli in the lungs of mammals and gills in fish. Figure 15.2 shows the features for gaseous exchange in an alveolus.

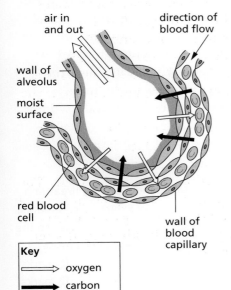

Figure 15.2

● **Try this** The answers are given on **p. 141**.

1 State how each feature labelled on the diagram of an alveolus makes the process of gaseous exchange efficient. [5 marks]

The composition of inspired and expired air

You need to be able to state the percentages shown in the table.

Gas	Inspired air/%	Expired air/%	Explanation
Nitrogen	79	79	Not used or produced by body processes
Oxygen	21	16	Used up in the process of respiration
Carbon dioxide	0.04	4	Produced in the process of respiration
Water vapour	Variable	Saturated	Produced in the process of respiration, moisture evaporates from the surface of the alveoli

Testing for carbon dioxide

Two chemical reagents can be used to test for carbon dioxide – they change colour when the gas is bubbled through. You only need to remember one.

- **Limewater** changes from colourless to milky.
- **Hydrogencarbonate** changes from red to yellow.

Expired air makes these reagents change colour more quickly than inspired air because there is more carbon dioxide present in expired air.

Effects of physical activity on breathing

The volume of air breathed in and out during normal, relaxed breathing is about 0.5 litres. This is the **tidal volume**. The breathing rate is about 12 breaths per minute.

During exercise, the volume inhaled (depth) increases to about 5 litres (depending on the age, sex, size and fitness of the person). The maximum amount of air breathed in or out in one breath is the **vital capacity**. The breathing rate can increase to over 20 breaths per minute. The total lung volume is greater than the vital capacity because some air always remains in the lungs (otherwise the lungs would collapse and the alveoli walls would stick together).

● **Try this** The answers are given on **p. 141**.

2 a) The composition of the air inside the lungs changes during breathing.
    i) State **three** differences between inspired and expired air. [3 marks]
    ii) Gaseous exchange in the alveoli causes some of the changes to the inspired air. Describe **three** features of the alveoli which assist gaseous exchange. [3 marks]
b) i) State what is meant by *anaerobic respiration*. [2 marks]
    ii) Where does anaerobic respiration occur in humans? [1 mark]

Effects of tobacco smoke on the respiratory system

Tobacco smoke contains a large number of toxic chemicals. The main ones are carbon monoxide, nicotine, smoke particles and tar. Note that these chemicals can affect other parts of the body as well as the respiratory system.

Chemical	Effects on respiratory system	Effects on other systems
Carbon monoxide	A poisonous gas. It combines with haemoglobin in red blood cells, preventing them from transporting oxygen	Increases the risk of atherosclerosis and thrombosis, which can lead to coronary heart disease
Nicotine	Addictive, resulting in the continuation of smoking, exposing the lungs to harmful chemicals	Raises blood pressure and heart rate Causes thrombosis and can lead to a stroke Stimulates the brain Can pass to the blood of a fetus from its mother, resulting in reduced birth weight
Smoke particles	Irritate the air passages, causing inflammation and increased mucus production, resulting in chronic bronchitis. Coughing and the presence of particles in the alveoli can lead to emphysema	
Tar	A carcinogen – increases the risk of lung cancer (cells start to divide out of control). Lines the air passages, increasing mucus production and paralysing and damaging cilia, causing bronchitis	

Common misconceptions

Remember that only nicotine and carbon monoxide enter the blood. Tar and smoke particles do not – they stay in the lungs. ■

Sample question and answer

Sample question The table shows the percentage of haemoglobin which is inactivated by carbon monoxide present in the blood of taxi drivers in a city.

City taxi drivers		Percentage of haemoglobin inactivated by carbon monoxide
Daytime drivers	Non-smokers	2.3
	Smokers	5.8
Night-time drivers	Non-smokers	1.0
	Smokers	4.4

i)   Suggest two sources of the carbon monoxide inhaled by these taxi drivers. [2 marks]

ii) Some daytime drivers have 5.8% of their haemoglobin affected. Using information from the table, explain which source contributes most to this effect. [2 marks]

iii) Suggest a reason for the differences, shown in the table, between daytime and night–time drivers. [1 mark]

continued

Student's answer **i)** 1. cigarette smoke ✓
2. breathing by passengers ✗
ii) It must be cigarette smoking ✓ because non-smokers have less of their haemoglobin affected. ✓
iii) There could be less car exhaust fumes, containing carbon monoxide, at night. ✓

Examiner's comments *In part (i), the second answer is biologically incorrect (we breathe out carbon dioxide, not carbon monoxide). The other correct answer was car exhaust gases. In part (ii), the answer and the explanation were correct. Part (iii) was a good answer.*

Role of ribs, intercostal muscles and diaphragm in ventilation of the lungs

Figure 15.3 shows the relationship between intercostal muscles, diaphragm and ribcage to achieve ventilation of the lungs.

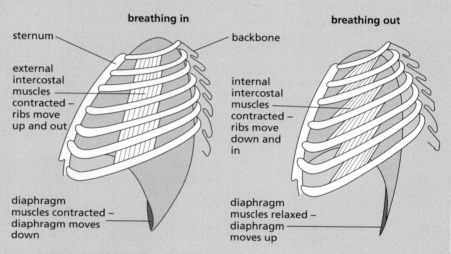

breathing in

sternum — backbone

external intercostal muscles contracted – ribs move up and out

internal intercostal muscles contracted – ribs move down and in

diaphragm muscles contracted – diaphragm moves down

breathing out

diaphragm muscles relaxed – diaphragm moves up

Figure 15.3

Breathing in (inhaling) Two sets of intercostal muscles are attached to the ribs. They are antagonistic (see Topic 18 for further details of antagonistic muscles).
When the external intercostal muscles contract, they move the ribcage upwards and outwards, increasing the volume of the thorax.
The diaphragm is a tough, fibrous sheet at the base of the thorax, with muscle around its edge. When the diaphragm muscle contracts, the diaphragm moves down, again increasing the volume of the thorax. This increase in volume reduces the air pressure in the thoracic cavity. As the air pressure outside the body is higher, air rushes into the lungs through the mouth or nose.

Breathing out (exhaling) The opposite happens when breathing out; during a forced exhalation the internal intercostal muscles contract and the diaphragm muscles relax. Thoracic volume decreases, so air pressure becomes greater than outside the body. Air rushes out of the lungs to equalise the pressure.

● **Try this** The answers are given on **p. 141**.

3 Write out the series of events involved in breathing in and breathing out as a set of bullet points, or as a flowchart linked with arrows.   [6 marks]

TOPIC 16 Excretion in humans

Key objectives

- To be able to define *excretion*
- To be able to describe the function of the kidney
- To be able to describe the relative positions of the ureters, bladder and urethra in the body
- To be able to describe the formation of urea and the breakdown of alcohol, drugs and hormones in the liver
- To be able to explain dialysis and discuss its application in kidney machines
- To be able to discuss the advantages and disadvantages of kidney transplants compared with dialysis

Key definition

Excretion	Removal from organisms of toxic materials, the waste products of metabolism, and substances in excess of requirements

Common misconceptions

Remember that faeces is **not** an example of excretion – it is mainly undigested material that has passed through the gut, but which has not been made in the body. The only excretory materials in it are bile pigments. ■

Figure 16.1 shows the relative positions of the kidneys, ureters, bladder and urethra in the body.

Key ideas

Function of the kidney

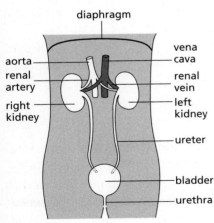

Figure 16.1

The function of the kidney is to filter blood, removing urea and excess water but reabsorbing glucose, some water and some mineral salts. The liquid produced is called urine – a solution of urea and mineral salts in water. The kidneys receive blood from the aorta (the main artery) via renal arteries. The renal artery splits into millions of capillaries, from which the blood is filtered under pressure. This forces all the small molecules and ions (such as glucose, urea, water and mineral salts) out of the capillary into a nephron. As the filtrate passes through the nephron, reabsorption takes place. Water is reabsorbed by osmosis, while glucose and mineral salts pass back into the blood by diffusion and active uptake (see Topic 6). The relative amount of water reabsorbed depends on the state of hydration of the body (how much water is in the blood), and is controlled by secretion of the hormone ADH. On a hot day, when we sweat more to cool down, the body needs to conserve water so we tend to produce a small amount of concentrated urine. On a cold day little sweat is being produced, so we tend to produce a larger volume of dilute urine. Filtered blood returns to the vena cava (main vein) via a renal vein.

The urine formed in the kidney passes down a ureter into the bladder, where it is stored. A sphincter muscle controls the release of urine through the urethra.

> **Examiner's tip**
> ▶ Make sure you can label the diagram (Figure 16.1) showing the relative positions of the kidneys, ureters, bladder and urethra. The spellings of the **ureter** and **urethra** are really important. Check that you get these spellings right, and that the structures are labelled in the correct positions.

Formation of urea and breakdown of alcohol, drugs and hormones in the liver

Surplus amino acids in the bloodstream cannot be stored. They are removed by the liver and broken down into urea (which is the nitrogen-containing part of the amino acid) and a sugar residue, which can be respired to release energy. The breakdown of amino acids is called **deamination**. Urea is returned to the bloodstream (into the hepatic vein) and filtered out when it reaches the kidneys.

The body treats alcohol as a poison. The liver removes poisons, such as alcohol and drugs, from the blood and breaks them down. Prolonged and excessive use of alcohol damages the liver and may cause it to fail. An overdose of drugs, such as paracetamol, can result in death due to liver failure, because the liver cannot cope with breaking down such a high concentration of the chemical.

The liver also converts hormones into inactive compounds. These are filtered out of the blood by the kidneys.

Sample question and answer

Sample question Figure 16.2 shows the human urinary system.
a) Name parts **X**, **Y** and **Z**. [3 marks]
b) Name the blood vessel that carries blood from the aorta to the kidneys. [1 mark]
c) Suggest two differences between the composition of the blood flowing to the kidneys and the blood flowing away from the kidneys. [2 marks]

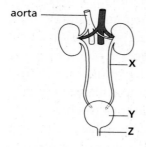

aorta

Figure 16.2

Student's answer
a) **X** ureta ✗ **Y** bladder ✓ **Z** vagina ✗
b) renal artery ✓
c) 1. Blood going to the kidneys contains more urea. ✓
   2. Blood going to the kidney contains oxygen. ✗

Examiner's comments *The spelling of **X** (ureter) must be accurate because this name is so similar to urethra. Part **Z** is the urethra, not the vagina (the vagina is attached to the uterus, not the bladder). In part (c), the second answer given does not make a comparison. If the candidate had stated 'blood going to the kidney contains **more** oxygen', this would have gained the mark.*

Dialysis and its application in kidney machines

Dialysis is a method of removing one or more components from a solution using the process of diffusion. The solution is separated from a bathing liquid by a partially permeable membrane (made of cellulose). The bathing liquid contains none of the components that need to be removed from the solution, so these pass from the solution, through the membrane, into the bathing solution by diffusion. The bathing solution needs to be changed regularly to maintain a concentration gradient.

The principle of dialysis is used in a kidney machine, as shown in Figure 16.3.

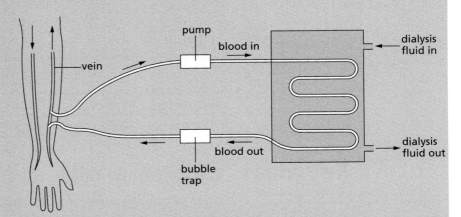

Figure 16.3

A patient with kidney failure needs to have toxic chemicals removed from the blood to stay alive. Blood is removed from a vein in the arm, and is kept moving through dialysis tubing in the dialysis machine using a pump. The tubing is very long to provide a large surface area. The dialysis fluid has a composition similar to blood plasma, but with no urea or uric acid. Urea, uric acid and excess mineral salts are removed from the blood, by diffusion, into the dialysis fluid. The cleaned blood is then passed through a bubble trap to remove any air bubbles, before being returned to the patient's vein.

Advantages and disadvantages of kidney transplants compared with dialysis

Advantages
- The patient can return to a normal lifestyle – dialysis may require a lengthy session in hospital, three times a week, leaving the patient very tired after each session.
- A dialysis machine will be available for other patients to use.
- Dialysis machines are expensive to buy and maintain.

Disadvantages
- Transplants require a suitable donor – with a good tissue match. The donor may be a dead person, or a close living relative who is prepared to donate a healthy kidney (we can survive with one kidney).
- The operation is very expensive.
- There is a risk of rejection of the donated kidney – immunosuppressive drugs have to be used (see Topic 14).
- Transplantation is not accepted by some religions.

TOPIC 17 Reactions to stimuli by plants and invertebrates

Key objectives
- To be able to define *tropism*, *geotropism* and *phototropism*
- To be able to describe simple behaviour in invertebrates
- To be able to describe the control of plant growth by auxins and the effects of synthetic plant hormones used as weedkillers
- To be able to describe phototropism and geotropism in terms of the role of auxins
- To be able to describe the effects of synthetic plant hormones used as weedkillers

Key definitions

Tropism	A plant growth response in which the direction of the response is determined by the direction of the stimulus
Geotropism	A plant growth response to gravity
Phototropism	A plant growth response to light

Key ideas

Simple behaviour in invertebrates

Some invertebrates react to stimuli using taxic responses (taxes). These are non-directional responses triggered by changes in the environment. Invertebrates tend to move around more rapidly in conditions they don't like (such as dry and bright) and less rapidly in ideal conditions (such as dark and moist).

A piece of apparatus called a choice chamber is shown in Figure 17.1. This can be used to demonstrate animal taxes.

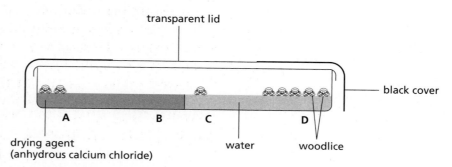

Figure 17.1 A choice chamber

In this investigation four different areas (**A–D**) have been set up with the following conditions:

A dry, dark
B dry, light
C damp, light
D damp, dark.

A fine mesh grill prevents the woodlice from being harmed by the drying agent or drowned in the water.

The woodlice are put in the centre of the choice chamber and allowed to move around for a few minutes. The number in each area is then counted. As a result of taxic behaviour, most collect in the damp, dark area.

Explanation: the response aids survival, as the woodlice are least likely to dehydrate in these conditions and less likely to be found by predators. Their food source (decaying leaves) is likely to be found here as well.

Plant responses (such as geotropism and phototropism) are directional responses, as plant shoots grow towards light and towards gravity. Details of these responses are only needed for Paper 3 (the Extension paper).

Control of plant growth by auxins

Auxins are plant growth substances. They are sometimes referred to as hormones, but this is not very accurate because they are not secreted by glands, and are not transported in blood. They are produced by the shoot and root tips of growing plants. An accumulation of auxin in a shoot stimulates cell growth by the absorption of water. However, auxins have the opposite effect in roots – when they build up, they slow down cell growth.

Phototropism and geotropism

These terms are explained in the Key definitions (page 66). You need to be able to describe the role of auxins in these processes.

Light When a shoot is exposed to light from one side, auxins that have been produced by the tip move towards the shaded side of the shoot (or the auxins are destroyed on the light side, causing an unequal distribution). Cells on the shaded side are stimulated to absorb **more** water than those on the light side, so the unequal growth causes the stem to bend towards the light. Growth of a shoot towards light is called **positive phototropism**.

If a root is exposed to light in the absence of gravity, auxins that have been produced by the tip move towards the shaded side of the root. Cells on the shaded side are stimulated to absorb **less** water than those on the light side, so the unequal growth causes the root to bend away from the light. Growth of a root away from light is called **negative phototropism**.

Gravity Shoots and roots also respond to gravity. If a shoot is placed horizontally in the absence of light, auxins accumulate on the lower side of the shoot, due to gravity. This makes the cells on the lower side grow **more quickly** than those on the upper side, so the shoot bends upwards. This is called **negative geotropism**.

If a root is placed horizontally in the absence of light, auxins also accumulate on the lower side of the root, due to gravity. However, this makes the cells on the lower side grow **more slowly** than those on the upper side, so the root bends downwards. This is called **positive geotropism**.

Shoots and roots that have their tips removed will not respond to light or gravity because the part that produces auxins has been cut off. Shoots that have their tips covered with opaque material grow straight upwards when exposed to one-sided light because the auxin distribution is not influenced by the light.

● **Try this** The answers are given on **p. 141**.

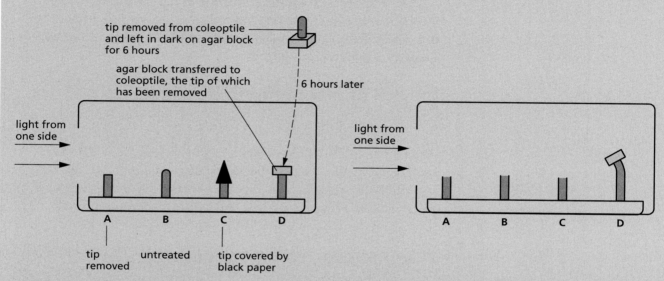

Figure 17.2

1 In Figure 17.2, the left-hand side shows an experiment in which the coleoptiles (shoots) of similar seedlings have been treated in different ways, and the right-hand side shows the result in shoot **D** 24 hours later.

a) i)   Name the response shown by shoot **D**. [2 marks]

   ii) Explain what has caused this response. [3 marks]

b) Copy and complete the right-hand side figure to show the likely results for shoots **A**, **B** and **C**. [3 marks]

c) i)   What name is given to the simple behavioural response shown by invertebrates to external stimuli? [1 mark]

   ii) Many invertebrates move towards damp and dark conditions when given a choice. Suggest how this response may help them to survive. [4 marks]

Effects of synthetic plant hormones used as weedkillers

Synthetic plant hormones are chemicals, similar to auxins, that have been manufactured. If they are sprayed on to plants they can cause rapid, uncontrolled growth and respiration resulting in the death of the plant. Some plant species are more sensitive than others to synthetic plant hormones, so weedkillers can be selective. Many weedkillers kill only broadleaved plants (dicotyledons), leaving grasses (monocotyledons) unharmed. Another term for a weedkiller is a **herbicide**.

TOPIC 18 Coordination and response

Key objectives
- To be able to define *hormone*
- To be able to describe the chemical control of metabolic activity by adrenaline
- To be able to describe the human nervous system
- To be able to define *sense organ*
- To be able to identify sensory and motor neurones from diagrams
- To be able to describe effectors
- To be able to describe the action of antagonistic muscles
- To be able to describe a reflex arc
- To be able to describe the structure and function of the eye
- To be able to compare nervous and hormonal control systems
- To be able to describe the effects of alcohol and heroin, and the dangers of their misuse – including personal and social problems
- To be able to define *homeostasis*
- To be able to describe temperature regulation
- To be able to distinguish between voluntary and involuntary actions
- To be able to distinguish between rods and cones
- To be able to describe the control of glucose content of the blood by the liver, insulin and glucagon
- To be able to describe the general role of negative feedback in homeostasis

Key definitions

Hormone	A chemical secreted by an endocrine gland. It is transported in the bloodstream and usually has a long-term effect on a target organ
Sense organ	A group of receptor cells responding to a specific stimulus, such as light, sound, touch, temperature, chemicals
Homeostasis	Maintenance of a constant internal environment

Key ideas

Chemical control of metabolic activity by adrenaline

The term **metabolism** describes all the chemical changes that take place in the body.

Adrenaline is a hormone secreted into the blood by the adrenal glands, which are found just above each kidney. It causes the heart rate to increase, so muscles are supplied with blood containing glucose and oxygen more quickly. This prepares them for action. Adrenaline also reduces the blood supply to the skin and digestive organs so blood is diverted to vital organs. It also stimulates the liver to convert glycogen to glucose.

The human nervous system

The human nervous system is made up of two parts:

- central nervous system – brain and spinal cord, which have the role of coordination
- peripheral nervous system – nerves, which connect all parts of the body to the central nervous system.

Sense organs are linked to the peripheral nervous system. They contain groups of receptor cells. When exposed to a stimulus they generate an electrical impulse which passes along peripheral nerves to the central nervous system, triggering a response. The table gives examples of sense organs and their stimuli.

Sense organ	Stimulus
Ear	Sound, body movement (balance)
Eye	Light
Nose	Chemicals (smell)
Tongue	Chemicals (taste)
Skin	Temperature, pressure, touch, pain

Peripheral nerves contain sensory and motor neurones (nerve cells). Sensory neurones transmit nerve impulses from sense organs to the central nervous system. Motor neurones transmit nerve impulses from the central nervous system to effectors (muscles or glands). Figure 18.1 shows the structures of neurones. You need to be able to recognise them from their features. Both types are covered with a myelin sheath, which insulates the neurone to make transmission of the impulse more efficient.

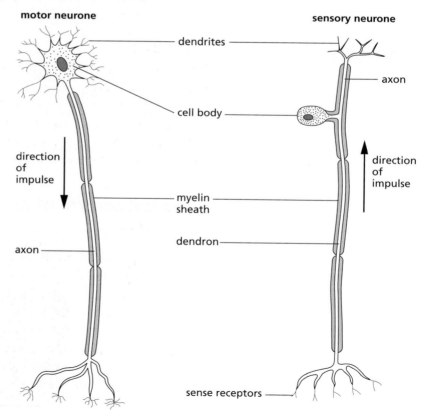

Figure 18.1

The cytoplasm (mainly axon and dendron) is elongated to transmit the impulse for long distances.

The table compares the structures of sensory and motor neurones.

Structure	Sensory neurone	Motor neurone
Cell body	Near end of neurone, in a ganglion (swelling) just outside the spinal cord	At start of neurone, inside the grey matter of the spinal cord
Dendrites	Present at end of neurone	Attached to cell body
Axon (part of neurone taking impulses away from cell body)	Very short	Very long
Dendron	Very long	None

Sample question and answer

Sample question

Figure 18.2

Figure 18.2 shows a type of neurone. Name this type of neurone and state a reason for your choice. [2 marks]

Student's answer   Name: motor neurone ✓
Reason: it has a cell body ✗

Examiner's comments   *The reason is not enough to distinguish it from other neurones – all neurones have cell bodies. If the answer had been extended to state that the cell body is at the end of the cell, it would have been awarded a mark.*

Effectors

Effectors are muscles or glands which respond when they receive impulses from motor neurones.

Examples of effectors are the biceps and triceps muscles in the arm. You need to be able to identify these muscles and the bones in the arm with which they are associated. Figure 18.3 shows the structure of the human arm.

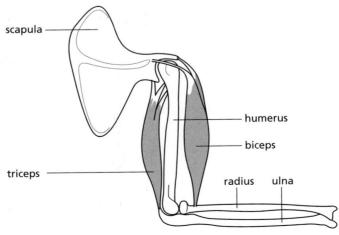

Figure 18.3

When stimulated, muscles contract (get shorter). The biceps and triceps are antagonistic muscles – they have opposite effects when they contract.

The biceps is attached to the scapula (shoulder blade) and the radius. Contraction of the biceps pulls on the radius, moving the lower arm towards the scapula. This results in the arm bending (flexing) at the elbow – the arm is raised.

The triceps is attached to the scapula, humerus and ulna. Contraction of the triceps pulls on the ulna, straightening (extending) the arm. In doing so, the triceps pulls the biceps back to its original length.

● **Try this**   The answers are given on **p. 142**.

1 Figure 18.4 is a simplified diagram of the muscles and bones of a human leg.

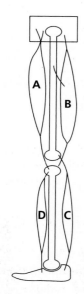

Figure 18.4

a) Copy and complete the following sentences.

Muscles are formed from cells which have the special property of being able to _____ . Because of this, muscles cannot push, they can only _____ .   [2 marks]

b) Muscles operate as antagonistic pairs. With reference to Figure 18.4, explain what is meant by this statement.   [2 marks]

c) i)   Which muscle, **A**, **B**, **C** or **D**, must contract in order to raise the heel to stand on tiptoe?   [1 mark]
   ii) Which muscle, **A**, **B**, **C** or **D**, must contract to bend the leg at the knee?   [1 mark]

d) When running very quickly, the muscles of the leg may not receive sufficient oxygen to supply all their energy requirements.
   i)   Name the type of respiration these muscle cells carry out to release additional energy.   [1 mark]
   ii) Name the waste product produced by this process.   [1 mark]

Simple reflex arcs

A reflex action is an automatic response to a stimulus. A reflex arc describes the pathway of an electrical impulse in response to a stimulus. Figure 18.5 on the next page shows a typical reflex arc. The stimulus is a drawing-pin sticking in the finger. The response is the withdrawal of the arm due to contraction of the biceps. Relay neurones are found in the spinal cord, connecting sensory neurones to motor neurones. Neurones do not connect directly with each other: there is a gap called a synapse. The impulse is 'transmitted' across the synapse by means of a chemical called acetylcholine.

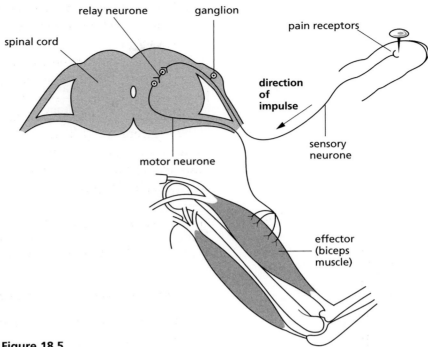

Figure 18.5

The sequence of events is:

Stimulus (sharp pin in finger)
↓
Receptor (pain receptor in skin)
↓
Coordinator (spinal cord)
↓
Effector (biceps muscle)
↓
Response (biceps muscle contracts, hand is withdrawn from pin)

● **Try this** The answers are given on **p. 142**.

2 Figure 18.6 shows a nerve cell.

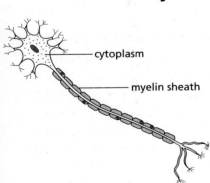

Figure 18.6

a) i) Name the type of nerve cell shown in the figure. [1 mark]
ii) State two features that distinguish it from other types of nerve cell. [2 marks]
iii) Where, in the nervous system, is this cell located? [1 mark]

b) Nerve cells are specialised cells. Suggest how the following parts of the nerve cell, labelled in the figure, enable the nerve cell to function successfully: *cytoplasm; myelin sheath*. [4 marks]

c) Reflexes involve a response to a stimulus.

i) Copy and complete the flowchart by putting the following terms in the boxes to show the correct sequence in a reflex. [2 marks]

coordinator effector receptor response stimulus

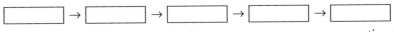

continued

ii) For the pupil reflex, identify each of the parts of the sequence by copying and completing the table below. The first has been done for you.

[4 marks]

Part of sequence	Part in pupil reflex
Coordinator	Brain
Effector	
Receptor	
Response	
Stimulus	

Structure and function of the eye

You need to be able to label parts of the eye on diagrams. Figures 18.7 and 18.8 show the front view of the eye, and a section through the left eye.

The eyebrow stops sweat running down into the eye. Eyelashes help to stop dust blowing on to the eye. Eyelids can close automatically (blinking is a reflex) to prevent dust and other particles getting on to the surface of the cornea. Blinking also helps to keep the surface moist by moving liquid secretions (tears) over the exposed surface. Tears also contain enzymes that have an antibacterial function.

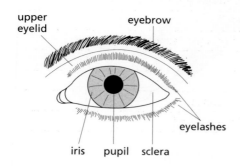

Figure 18.7

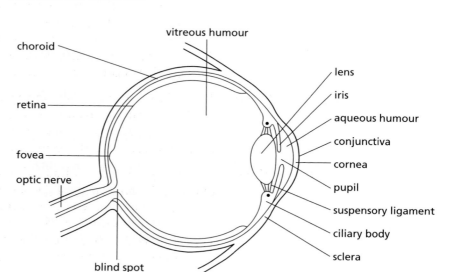

Figure 18.8

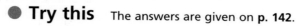

● **Try this**   The answers are given on **p. 142**.

3 Trace or copy both diagrams of the eye. Practice adding the labels.

[8 marks]

The table gives the functions of parts of the eye.

Part	Function
Aqueous humour	Transparent, colourless, watery liquid in front of the lens, that maintains the shape of the cornea
Blind spot	Part of the retina in front of the optic nerve that lacks rods or cones
Choroid	Produces a black pigment to prevent reflection of light inside the eye
Ciliary body	A ring of muscle that controls the shape of the lens to allow focusing
Conjunctiva	A transparent, sensitive layer on the surface of the cornea
Cornea	A transparent layer at the front of the eye that refracts the light entering to help to focus it
Fovea	An area of the retina containing a high concentration of cones, where light is usually focused and colours are detected
Iris	A coloured ring of circular and radial muscle that controls the size of the pupil
Lens	A transparent, convex, flexible, jelly-like structure that refracts light to focus it
Optic nerve	Transmits electrical impulses from the retina to the brain
Pupil	A hole in the centre of the iris that controls the amount of light reaching the retina
Retina	A light-sensitive layer made up of rods and cones
Sclera	A tough, white layer that protects the eyeball
Suspensory ligament	Attaches the lens to the ciliary body, so the lens is held in place
Vitreous humour	Transparent, viscous liquid that maintains the shape of the eyeball

Accommodation

The amount of focusing needed by the lens depends on the distance of the object being viewed – light from near objects requires a more convex lens than light from a distant object. The shape of the lens needed to accommodate the image is controlled by the ciliary body – this contains a ring of muscle around the lens.

Distant objects The ciliary muscles relax, giving them a larger diameter. This pulls on the suspensory ligaments which, in turn, pull on the lens. This makes the lens thinner (less convex). As the ciliary muscles are relaxed, there is no strain on the eye (Figure 18.9, left-hand side).

Near objects The ciliary muscles contract, giving them a smaller diameter. This removes the tension on the suspensory ligaments which, in turn, stop pulling on the lens. The lens becomes thicker (more convex) (Figure 18.9, right-hand side). As the ciliary muscles are contracted, there is strain on the eye, which can cause a headache if a near object (book, microscope, computer screen, etc.) is viewed for too long.

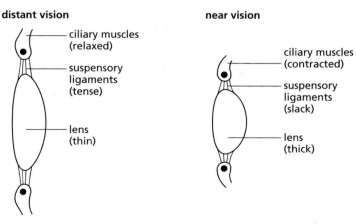

Figure 18.9 Accommodation in the eye

75

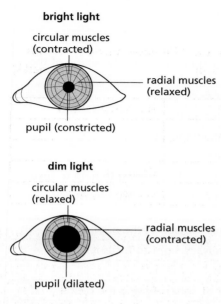

bright light

circular muscles
(contracted)

radial muscles
(relaxed)

pupil (constricted)

dim light

circular muscles
(relaxed)

radial muscles
(contracted)

pupil (dilated)

Figure 18.10

Pupil reflex

This reflex changes the size of the pupil to control the amount of light entering the eye. In bright light, pupil size is reduced as too much light falling on the retina could damage it. In dim light, pupil size is increased to allow as much light as possible to enter the eye. Figure 18.10 shows the effect of light intensity on the iris and pupil.

The retina detects the brightness of light entering the eye. An impulse passes to the brain along sensory neurones and travels back to the muscles of the iris along motor neurones, triggering a response – the change in size of the pupil due to contraction of radial or circular muscles.

Common misconceptions

Students often confuse circular muscles and ciliary muscles. Remember that circular muscles affect the size of the iris; ciliary muscles affect the shape of the lens. ■

● **Try this** The answers are given on **p. 142**.

4 Describe and explain how the eye changes its focus from a distant object to a near object. [5 marks]

Comparing nervous and hormonal control systems

The table shows the main differences between these systems.

Feature	Nervous	Hormonal (endocrine)
Form of transmission	Electrical impulses	Chemical (hormones)
Transmission pathway	Nerves	Blood vessels
Speed of transmission	Fast	Slow
Duration of effect	Short term	Long term
Response	Localised	Widespread (although there may be a specific target organ)

● **Try this**   The answers are given on **p. 142**.

5 Copy and complete the table to show the differences between nervous and hormonal control in the human body.   [4 marks]

Feature	Nervous control	Hormonal control
Speed	Extremely rapid	
Pathway	Neurones	
Nature of 'impulse'		Chemical
Origin		Endocrine gland

Distinguishing between voluntary and involuntary actions

A voluntary action involves the brain in its initiation – it involves conscious thought, as we make a decision about making the action. Involuntary actions are generally reflexes, which cannot be overridden. They are initiated by sense receptors, which generate electrical impulses. Involuntary actions are automatic, which makes them faster than voluntary actions. Activities inside the body, such as heartbeat and peristalsis, are controlled involuntarily.

Distinguishing between rods and cones

Rods and cones are light-sensitive cells in the retina. When stimulated they generate electrical impulses, which pass to the brain along the optic nerve.

The table shows the main differences between rods and cones.

	Function	Distribution	Comments
Rods	Sensitive to low light intensity. Detect shades of grey	Found throughout the retina, but none in the centre of the fovea or in the blind spot	Provide us with night vision, when we can recognise shapes but not colours
Cones	Sensitive only to high light intensity. Detect colour (don't operate in poor light)	Concentrated in the fovea	There are three types, sensitive to red, green and blue light

Drugs

Drugs may be used to treat disease, reduce the sensation of pain, or help calm us down. In addition, they may change our mood by affecting the brain. Depressants have a relaxing effect because they depress the central nervous system. In high doses they can lead to sleep or act as an anaesthetic, causing unconsciousness. You need to be able to describe the effects of alcohol and heroin, the dangers of their misuse and the personal and social problems they can cause.

Drug	Effects	Dangers
Alcohol	Small amounts – alcohol can relax the body and create a sense of wellbeing. However, alcohol is a depressant: larger amounts slow down the transmission of electrical impulses in the brain, so reactions are depressed, coordination is impaired and reasoned judgements become difficult. Mood swings involving violence can result	Increased reaction time makes driving and handling machinery dangerous. Poor judgements may lead to criminal activity and sexual promiscuity Long-term excessive drinking can lead to addiction (alcoholism) This can lead to financial difficulties and family problems As the liver removes alcohol from the blood, heavy drinking can lead to liver damage such as cirrhosis. Drinking can cause brain damage, peptic ulcers in the stomach and obesity Drinking during pregnancy can damage the fetus, increase the risk of miscarriage or premature birth, and reduce the average birth weight
Heroin	Heroin is a narcotic, producing a dream-like feeling of relaxation and reducing severe pain. However, it is very addictive, leading to dependency (addiction). Withdrawal symptoms can be very unpleasant – involving cramp, sleeplessness, violent vomiting, sweating and hallucinations	The body develops a tolerance to the drug, so an addict needs to take increasing amounts to achieve the same feeling. This leads to the risk of overdosing on the drug When injected using unsterilised and shared needles, there is a risk of infections such as hepatitis and HIV Addiction creates financial problems leading to family breakdown, criminal activity and sexual promiscuity

● **Try this**   The answers are given on **p. 142**.

6 a) Alcohol is described as a depressant and an addictive drug that can damage the body.

   i)   State what is meant by each of the following terms: *depressant*; *addictive*. [2 marks]

   ii) State two long-term effects that alcohol might have on the body. [2 marks]

   b) Suggest how alcohol might affect the performance of a car driver. [2 marks]

Homeostasis – temperature regulation

Maintaining a constant internal environment is vital for an organism to stay healthy. Fluctuations in temperature, water levels and nutrient concentrations, for example, could lead to death. Temperature regulation is one homeostatic function. Mammals and birds are warm-blooded – they maintain a constant body temperature despite external environment changes. Humans maintain a body temperature of 37°C – we have mechanisms to lose heat when we get too hot, and ways of retaining heat when we get too cold. Figure 18.11 summarises two ways of regulating body temperature.

Sweating   Sweat is a liquid made up of water, salts and some urea. Sweat glands in the skin secrete sweat through pores on to the skin surface. As the water in the sweat evaporates, it removes heat from

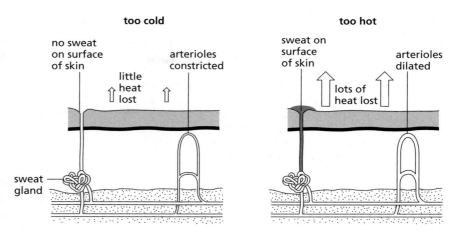

Figure 18.11

the skin, cooling it down. When we are too hot, the volume of sweat produced increases. Prolonged sweating can lead to dehydration and shortage of salts. If we get too cold, the amount of sweat produced is reduced.

Vasodilation/ vasoconstriction

Recall that heat is transported around the body in the bloodstream (page 55). When blood passes through blood vessels near the skin surface, heat is lost by radiation. Arterioles (small arteries) have muscle in their walls.

When we are too hot, these muscles relax, creating a wide lumen through which lots of blood can pass (the skin of a hot person may look red). This is called **vasodilation**. More heat is radiated, so we cool down.

When we are too cold, the muscles contract, creating a narrow lumen through which little blood can pass (the skin of a cold person may look very pale). This is called **vasoconstriction**. Less heat is radiated, to conserve heat.

Common misconceptions

Remember that the processes of vasodilation and vasoconstriction happen only in arterioles – they do **not** happen in capillaries or veins. When writing about the processes, make sure you refer to arterioles. ■

Control of glucose content in blood

The liver is a homeostatic organ – it controls the levels of a number of materials in the blood, including glucose. Two hormones – insulin and glucagon – control blood glucose levels. Both hormones are secreted by the pancreas and are transported to the liver in the bloodstream. Excess glucose is stored in the liver and muscles as the polysaccharide glycogen (animal starch).

continued

When glucose levels drop below normal, glycogen is broken down to glucose, which is released into the bloodstream.

blood glucose
levels too high
                              insulin
                    glucose ⇌ glycogen
blood glucose   glucagon
levels too low

If blood glucose levels get too high or too low, they can result in the person losing consciousness, falling into a coma and dying. This is why diabetics have to monitor and control their blood glucose levels through diet and the injection of insulin. Insulin cannot be taken by mouth – this hormone is a protein, which would be digested in the stomach. As well as stimulating the conversion of glucose to glycogen, insulin also increases the rate of respiration (in which glucose is broken down), so more blood glucose is absorbed by cells and used up.

Examiner's tip

► Be accurate with the spellings of **glycogen** and **glucagon** and make sure you do not muddle these terms up.

● **Try this**   The answers are given on **p. 142**.

7 Copy and complete the paragraph using some of the words in the list below.

excretion	glucose	glycogen	insulin	liver	oestrogen
pancreas	secretion	starch	stomach	sucrose	

The bloodstream transports a sugar called _____ . The blood sugar level has to be kept constant in the body. If this level falls below normal, a hormone called glucagon is released into the blood by an endocrine organ called the _____ . The release of a substance from a gland is called _____ . Glucagon promotes the breakdown of _____ to increase the blood sugar level. If the blood sugar level gets too high, the endocrine organ secretes another hormone called _____ into the blood. This hormone promotes the removal of sugar from the blood and its conversion to glycogen in the _____ .   [6 marks]

Role of negative feedback in homeostasis

A change from normal, for instance an increase in blood glucose levels, triggers a sensor, which stimulates a response in an effector. However, the response – in this case the secretion of insulin – would eventually result in glucose levels dropping below normal. As glucose levels drop, the sensor detects the drop and instructs an effector (the pancreas) to stop secreting insulin. This is negative feedback – the change is fed back to the effector

TOPIC 19 Reproduction, growth and development in plants

Key objectives

- To be able to define *asexual* and *sexual reproduction*
- To be able to describe asexual reproduction in bacteria, fungi and potatoes
- To be able to describe the structure and functions of a dicotyledonous flower in relation to sexual reproduction
- To be able to define *pollination* and name the agents of pollination
- To be able to compare the structural adaptations of insect-pollinated and wind-pollinated flowers
- To be able to describe the events leading to fertilisation
- To be able to describe the formation of a seed and fruit
- To be able to define *dispersal* of *seeds* and *fruits*
- To be able to describe seed and fruit dispersal by wind and animals
- To be able to define *growth* and *development*
- To be able to describe the environmental conditions affecting germination
- To be able to discuss the advantages and disadvantages of asexual and sexual reproduction
- To be able to discuss the implications for a species of self-pollination and cross-pollination

Key definitions

Asexual reproduction	Formation of a new organism, without the involvement of gametes or fertilisation
Sexual reproduction	Formation of a new organism by the fusion of gametes (fertilisation)
Pollination	Transfer of pollen grains from the anther to the stigma
Dispersal	A means of moving fruits or seeds away from the parent plant
Growth	An increase in dry mass of an organism as a result of cell growth and division
Development	An increase in complexity through the differentiation of cells

Key ideas ## Asexual reproduction

Examples of organisms that show this form of reproduction include bacteria, fungi and potatoes. These are described in Figure 19.1.

Bacteria	Fungi	Potatoes
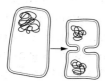	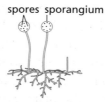	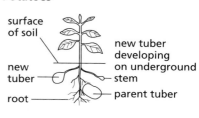
Bacteria reproduce asexually by binary fission. Inside an individual bacterium, the DNA replicates. Then the cell divides into two, with each daughter cell containing a copy of the parental DNA. Once the daughter cells have grown, they can also reproduce	Fungi can reproduce asexually by producing spores, which may be formed inside a structure called a sporangium. When ripe, the sporangium bursts open allowing the spores to be dispersed. In suitable conditions the spores germinate and grow to form new individuals	Potatoes are stem tubers. The parent plant photosynthesises and stores the food produced in underground stems, which swell to form tubers. Each tuber contains stored starch, and there are buds in depressions in the surface known as eyes. In suitable conditions the buds use the stored food to form shoots, from which roots also develop. Each tuber can form a new plant

Figure 19.1 Asexual reproduction

Advantages and disadvantages of asexual reproduction

Advantages and disadvantages to a species of asexual reproduction are listed in the table.

Advantages	Disadvantages
• The process is quick	• There is little variation created, so adaptation to a changing environment (evolution) is unlikely
• Only one parent is needed	• If the parent has no resistance to a particular disease, none of the offspring will have resistance
• No gametes are needed	• Lack of dispersal (e.g. potato tubers) can lead to competition for nutrients, water and light
• All the good characteristics of the parent are passed on to the offspring	
• Where there is no dispersal (e.g. in potato tubers), offspring will grow in the same favourable environment as the parent	
• Plants that reproduce asexually usually store large amounts of food that allow rapid growth when conditions are suitable	

Advantages and disadvantages of sexual reproduction

These are listed in the table.

Advantages	Disadvantages
• There is variation in the offspring so adaptation to a changing or new environment is likely, enabling survival of the species	• Two parents are usually needed (though not always – some plants can self-pollinate)
• New varieties can be created, which may have resistance to disease	• Growth of a new plant to maturity from a seed is slow
• In plants, seeds are produced, which allow dispersal away from the parent plant, reducing competition	

Sexual reproduction in plants

You need to be able to describe the structure and functions of a named dicotyledonous flower. Dicotyledonous plants produce seeds with two cotyledons, and also have other characteristics that separate them from monocotyledonous plants (such as grasses and tulips), but you do not need any details for this syllabus. Figure 19.2 shows the main parts of a lupin flower that has been cut in half. Other flowers have the same features, but the numbers and relative sizes of the parts vary.

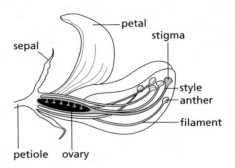

Figure 19.2

Functions of parts of a flower

The table shows the main functions of the parts of a flower.

Part	Function
Petal	Often large and coloured, to attract insects
Sepal	Protects the flower while in bud
Petiole (stalk)	Supports the flower to make it easily seen by insects, and to be able to withstand wind
Nectary	Produces nectar, to attract insects
Stamen	The male reproductive part of the flower, made up of anther and filament
Anther	Contains pollen sacs, in which pollen grains are formed. Pollen contains male sex cells
Filament	Supports the anther
Carpel	The female reproductive part of the flower, made up of stigma, style and ovary
Stigma	A sticky surface that receives pollen during pollination
Style	Links the stigma to the ovary, through which pollen tubes grow
Ovary	Contains ovules, which develop into seeds when fertilised

Agents of pollination

Flowers are usually pollinated by insects or wind. The structural adaptations of a flower depend on the type of pollination the plant uses.

Comparing the structural adaptations of insect- and wind-pollinated flowers

Figure 19.3 shows the structure of a grass flower, which is wind-pollinated. Although you do not need to be able to draw this, you do need to be able to compare insect- and wind-pollinated flowers.

The table compares the features of wind- and insect-pollinated flowers.

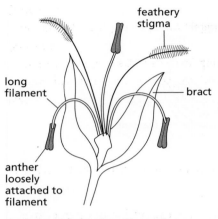

Figure 19.3 Wind-pollinated grass flower

Feature	Insect-pollinated	Wind-pollinated
Petals	Present – often large, coloured and scented, with guidelines to guide insects into the flower	Absent, or small and inconspicuous
Nectar	Produced by nectaries to attract insects	Absent, or small and green
Stamen	Present inside the flower	Long filaments, allowing the anthers to hang freely outside the flower so the pollen is exposed to the wind
Stigmas	Small surface area, inside the flower	Large and feathery, hanging outside the flower to catch pollen carried by the wind
Pollen	Smaller amounts – grains are often round and sticky, or covered in spikes to attach to the furry bodies of insects	Larger amounts of smooth and light pollen grains, which are easily carried by the wind
Bracts (modified leaves)	Absent	Sometimes present

Common misconceptions

Students often get confused between pollination and seed dispersal. When animals such as insects carry pollen, they aid pollination. When animals carry seeds, they aid seed dispersal. ■

Growth of pollen tube and the process of fertilisation

Figure 19.4 shows a section through a single carpel. If pollen grains are of the same species as the flower they land on, they may germinate. Germination is triggered by a sugary solution on the stigma, and involves the growth of a pollen tube from the pollen grain. The pollen tube contains the male nucleus, which is needed to fertilise the ovule inside the ovary. The pollen tube grows down the style, through the ovary wall, and through the micropyle of the ovule. Fertilisation is the fusion of the male nucleus with the female nucleus. If the ovary contains a lot of ovules, each will need to be fertilised by a different pollen nucleus.

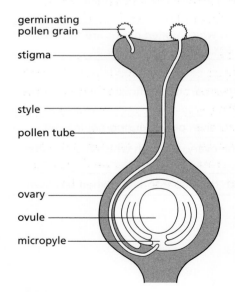

Figure 19.4

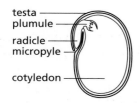

Figure 19.5

Formation of seed and fruit

The fertilised ovule divides by mitosis to form a seed containing the embryo plant and food stores called cotyledons. The wall of the ovule forms the seed testa (coat). The ovary wall develops into a fruit, which may be fleshy (e.g. plum) or a dry pod (e.g. lupin or pea). Figure 19.5 shows the structure of a non-endospermic seed.

● **Try this**   The answers are given on **p. 142**.

1 Figure 19.6 shows a section through a bean flower.

   a) Name the parts labelled **A** and **B**. [2 marks]

   b) This flower is insect-pollinated. Suggest how parts **C**, **D** and **E** help in pollination of this flower. [3 marks]

   c) After pollination, the ovules develop into seeds. Describe the events which occur after pollination and which result in the formation of seeds. [4 marks]

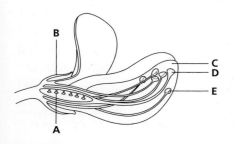

Figure 19.6

Seed dispersal

You need to be able to describe the dispersal of fruits and seeds by wind and animals.

Wind-dispersed fruits

Wind-dispersed fruits contain seeds, and usually have a parachute or a wing to help them be carried away from the parent plant by the wind. Examples of wind dispersal, illustrated in Figure 19.7, include dandelion and sycamore.

The dandelion fruit has a group of fine hairs called a pappus, which catches the wind and acts like a parachute. The fruit counterbalances the pappus.

The sycamore has a wing with a large surface area. When the fruit drops off the tree it spins, slowing down its descent. If caught by the wind the seed will be carried away from the parent plant, reducing competition for nutrients, water and light.

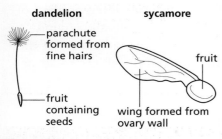

Figure 19.7

Animal-dispersed fruits

There are two main modifications of fruits for animal dispersal: succulent fruits and hooked fruits. Examples of each of these are illustrated in Figure 19.8.

Succulent fruits attract animals because they are brightly coloured, juicy and nutritious. When eaten, the seeds pass through the animal's gut without being digested and are deposited with the animal's faeces, which may be a long way from the parent plant. The faeces provides nutrients when the seeds germinate.

Hooked fruits catch on to an animal's fur as it brushes past the parent plant. Eventually the seeds drop off, or the animal grooms itself to remove them. This disperses the seeds away from the parent plant.

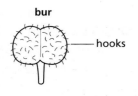

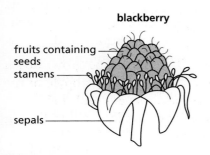

Figure 19.8

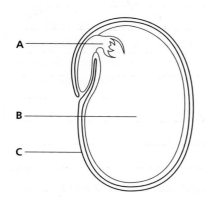

Figure 19.9

● **Try this**   The answers are given on **p. 142**.

2 Figure 19.9 shows a section through a bean seed.

a) i)   Name the parts labelled **A**, **B** and **C**.   [3 marks]
   ii)   Copy or trace the diagram and label with an **X** the part that
         contains the seed's food reserves.   [1 mark]

b) Seeds and fruits are dispersed away from the parent plant.
   i)   Sketch a seed or fruit that is adapted for dispersal by wind. Label
         with a **Y** the special feature of the seed or fruit that helps in wind
         dispersal.   [1 mark]
   ii)   Suggest how this feature helps in wind dispersal.   [2 marks]
   iii) Suggest another way in which wind assists in the reproduction of
         plants.   [1 mark]

Self-pollination and cross-pollination

Self-pollination involves the transfer of pollen from the anther
to the stigma of the same flower, or to another flower of the same
plant. Smaller numbers of pollen grains need to be produced,
because there is a greater chance of successful pollination. This
increases the chance of fertilisation and seed formation, but
reduces the variation in the offspring. Self-pollinated plants are
less likely to cope with adapting to environmental change.

   Cross-pollination involves the transfer of pollen from the
anther of a flower to the stigma of a flower on a different plant of
the same species. This reduces the chance of fertilisation (wind-
pollinated flowers produce large amounts of pollen because of the
wastage involved), but increases variation and the ability to adapt
to environmental change.

Growth and development

Growth   Growth is due to an increase in cells, produced by mitosis. In
animals it is controlled by hormones, and in plants by growth
substances such as auxins.

   Dry mass is often used as a measure of growth, because wet mass
varies from day to day (e.g. plants will take up more water on a wet
day than on a dry day, but the water does not all become part of the
biomass – living material – of the plant). The value of the dry mass is
obtained by drying out the organism in an oven, but this involves
killing it. To monitor the growth of a plant, many individuals have
to be germinated at the same time and grown in the same conditions.
Samples are then taken and dried at various times during the growth
period. Figure 19.10 shows the growth of a plant from a seed.

   There is a small drop in dry mass as the seed germinates
(at 2 days). This because some of the food stores in the cotyledon
are being used in respiration. Dry mass increases as soon as the
plumule starts to photosynthesise, and foliage leaves form to
continue the process. Annual plants grow quickly. Dry mass
decreases at the end of the growth period because of the loss of
seeds and fruits, or as leaves die.

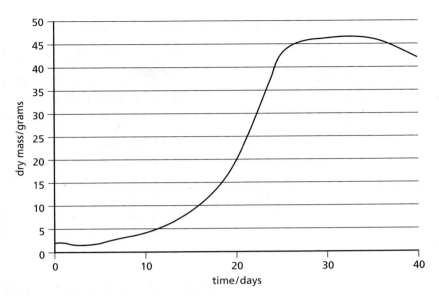

Figure 19.10

Growth may also be measured using wet (or fresh) mass, height, surface area (e.g. of leaves), volume, number of leaves and body length. Human growth is usually measured using height or body mass. However, neither of these is ideal – some people are tall and thin while others are short and broad; increases in mass may be due to the storage of fat, which is not really growth. Organs grow at different rates at different times – the brain reaches its adult size at or before puberty, but other organs continue to grow.

Development Development is the increase in complexity of an organism as it grows. As the number of cells increases, they become differentiated (they specialise to carry out different tasks). This involves changes in shape to adapt for a specific function. For example, nerve cells are very elongated and can transmit electrical impulses; xylem cells are elongated and lose their cell contents, with the cell walls becoming lignified so the cells conduct water efficiently. In humans, stages in development such as puberty are triggered by hormones which, in turn, can create a growth spurt.

● **Try this** The answers are given on **p. 143**.

3 a) Figure 19.11 shows a section through a seed of a dicotyledon.

    i) What is the role of part **A**?   [1 mark]

    ii) What do parts **B** and **C** of the seed develop into after germination?   [2 marks]

b) Figure 19.12 on the next page shows changes in mass of sets of pea seeds as they germinate and grow into seedlings. After germination, set **P** was grown in the dark and set **Q** in the light.

    i) Why is mass measured as dry mass?   [1 mark]

    ii) Explain the changes in dry mass between days **X** and **Y** in both sets of seedlings.   [4 marks]

    iii) Explain why there is a difference in the dry mass of sets **P** and **Q** between days **Y** and **Z**.   [4 marks]

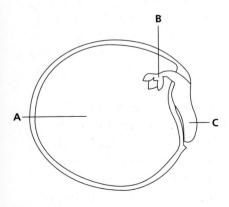

Figure 19.11

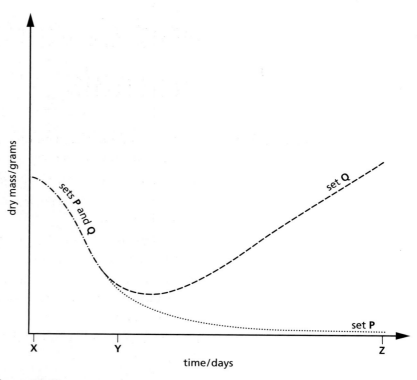

Figure 19.12

Environmental conditions affecting germination

A seed is a living structure. It contains an embryo which will germinate and develop into an adult plant if provided with suitable conditions. These are listed and explained in the table.

Environmental condition	Explanation
Water	This is absorbed through the micropyle until the radicle has forced its way out of the testa. It is needed to activate enzymes which convert insoluble food stores into soluble foods that can be used for growth and energy production
Oxygen	This is needed for respiration, to release energy for growth and the chemical changes needed for mobilisation of food reserves
Suitable temperature	Enzymes work best at an optimum temperature. Generally, the higher the temperature (up to 40°C), the faster the rate of germination. However, some seeds need a period of chilling before they will germinate. Low temperatures usually maintain dormancy – if the seed germinated in unsuitable conditions, it would be unlikely to survive
Light	This is not usually a requirement for germination (seeds germinate under soil), but some seeds, such as lettuce, do need a period of exposure to light before they will germinate

TOPIC 20 Reproduction, growth and development in animals

Key objectives

- To be able to describe the structure and functions of parts of the male and female reproductive systems
- To be able to describe the menstrual cycle
- To be able to describe sexual intercourse, fertilisation and implantation
- To be able to describe the development of the fetus, the role of ante-natal care and birth
- To be able to describe the roles of oestrogen and testosterone in the development and regulation of secondary sexual characteristics at puberty
- To be able to name and describe the main methods of birth control
- To be able to describe the symptoms, signs, effects and treatment of gonorrhoea
- To be able to describe the methods of transmission of HIV and the ways it can be prevented from spreading
- To be able to state the functions of the amniotic sac and amniotic fluid
- To be able to describe the advantages of breastfeeding compared with bottle-feeding
- To be able to describe the production and roles of hormones in the menstrual cycle and in pregnancy
- To be able to discuss the social aspects of artificial insemination and the use of hormones in fertility drugs
- To be able to outline how HIV affects the immune system

Key ideas

Structure and functions of parts of the male reproductive system

front   side

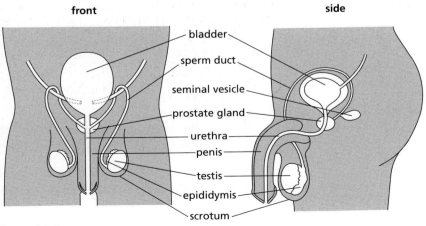

bladder
sperm duct
seminal vesicle
prostate gland
urethra
penis
testis
epididymis
scrotum

Figure 20.1

The table shows the functions of the main parts of the male reproductive system.

Part	Function
Epididymis	A mass of tubes in which sperm are stored
Penis	Can become firm, to insert into the vagina of the female during sexual intercourse, to transfer sperm
Prostate gland	Adds fluid and nutrients to sperm, to form semen
Scrotum	A sac that holds the testes outside the body, keeping them cooler than body temperature
Seminal vesicle	Adds fluid and nutrients to sperm, to form semen
Sperm duct	Muscular tube which links the testis to the urethra to allow the passage of semen containing sperm
Testis	Male gonads that produce sperm
Urethra	To pass semen containing sperm through the penis, also carries urine from the bladder at different times

Structure and functions of parts of the female reproductive system

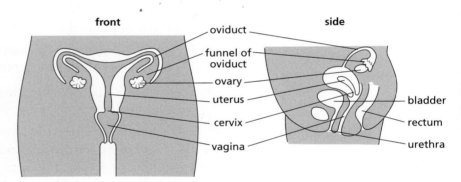

Figure 20.2

Part	Function
Cervix	A ring of muscle that separates the vagina from the uterus
Funnel of oviduct	Directs an ovum (egg) from the ovary into the oviduct
Ovary	Contains follicles in which ova (eggs) are produced
Oviduct	Carries an ovum to the uterus, with propulsion provided by tiny cilia in the wall; also the site of fertilisation
Urethra	Carries urine from the bladder
Uterus	Where the fetus develops
Vagina	Receives the male penis during sexual intercourse; sperm are deposited here

Common misconceptions

Terms such as **urethra** and **ureter** are often confused or misspelt. Make sure you can write the correct spellings and label these parts correctly. ■

The menstrual cycle

This is a cycle involving changes in the uterus and ovaries, controlled by a number of hormones. Each cycle takes about 28 days (Figure 20.3).

- At the start of each cycle, menstruation occurs – the lining of the uterus breaks down due to a drop in the level of **progesterone**, and the cells and blood making up the lining are shed via the vagina. This is **menstruation**.
- Under the influence of **oestrogen** from the ovaries, the uterus lining then starts to build up again, developing a mass of blood vessels so it is ready to receive a fertilised ovum.

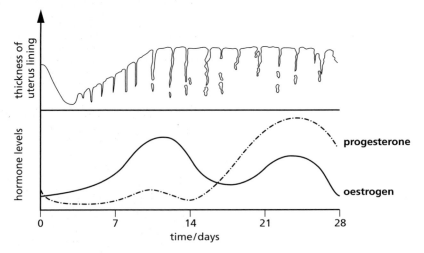

Figure 20.3

- **Follicle stimulating hormone** (FSH) causes a follicle in one of the ovaries to mature into an ovum.
- About half-way through the cycle, the level of **oestrogen** drops and there is a secretion of the hormone **LH** (**luteinizing hormone**) from the pituitary gland, triggering ovulation. This is when the wall of the ovary ruptures and an ovum is released.
- The remains of the follicle (now called the corpus luteum) starts to secrete **progesterone**, which maintains the uterus lining.
- Towards the end of the cycle, the corpus luteum breaks down resulting in a drop in secretion of **progesterone**. The lining of the uterus breaks down again.

Formation and development of the fetus

Sexual intercourse involves inserting the erect penis into the vagina. When stimulated, spongy tissue in the penis fills with blood and becomes erect. At the climax, semen is ejaculated from the penis into the neck of the vagina. Muscles in the wall of the sperm ducts help to propel the semen forwards. Using their tails, the sperm swim from the vagina, through the cervix and uterus, into an oviduct.

   Fertilisation may occur if there is an ovum passing down the oviduct. A single sperm penetrates the membrane of the ovum by secreting a protease enzyme. The sperm nucleus fuses with the ovum nucleus to form a zygote. A zygote is a single cell formed as the result of the fusion of two gametes.

91

Sperm can remain active in the oviduct for at least 2 days and the ovum may take a day to pass from the ovary to the uterus, so there is a fertile period of 3 to 4 days around ovulation when fertilisation can happen.

The zygote starts to divide by mitosis to form a ball of cells (a blastula). It continues to move down the oviduct until it reaches the uterus.

Implantation occurs when the blastula embeds in the lining of the uterus.

Development of the fetus – the blastula develops into an embryo and some of the cells form a placenta, linking the embryo with the uterus lining. Organs such as the heart develop and, after 8 weeks, the embryo is called a fetus. Growth of the fetus requires a good supply of nutrients and oxygen. This is achieved through the link between the placenta and the mother's blood supply in the uterus lining (see Figure 20.4).

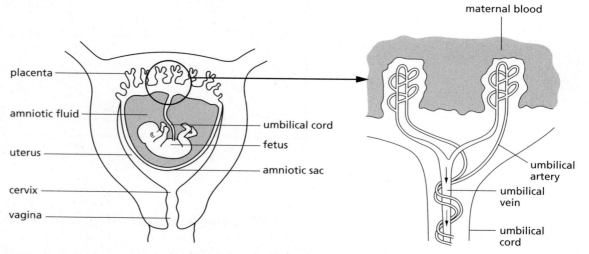

Figure 20.4

The placenta brings the blood supply of the fetus close to that of the mother, but prevents mixing. This is really important because the fetus and mother may have different blood groups – any mixing could result in blood clotting, which could be fatal to both mother and fetus. Blood from the fetus passes through the umbilical cord in the umbilical artery to the placenta. Here it comes close to the mother's blood. Oxygen, amino acids, glucose and other nutrients diffuse into the blood of the fetus. Carbon dioxide, urea and other wastes pass into the mother's blood. Blood returns to the fetus through the umbilical vein.

● **Try this** The answers are given on **p. 143**.

1 Figure 20.5 shows a fetus developing in the uterus.

a) i)   Copy the figure, and label parts **A** and **B**. [2 marks]
    ii) Outline **three** functions of the placenta. [3 marks]
    iii) The blood of the fetus and that of the mother flow close to each other in the placenta, but do not mix. State **two** advantages to the fetus of having a separate blood system from that of the mother. [2 marks]

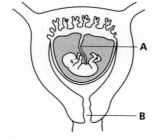

Figure 20.5

Functions of the amniotic sac and amniotic fluid

The **amniotic sac** is a membrane, formed from cells of the embryo, which contains the amniotic fluid. It encloses the developing fetus and prevents entry of bacteria.

Amniotic fluid supports the fetus, protecting it from physical damage. It absorbs excretory materials (urine) released by the fetus.

Sample question and answer

Sample question Figure 20.6 shows a fetus developing in the uterus. Copy and complete the table below by identifying the parts labelled **A**, **B** and **C** and stating a function of each one.

Part	Name	Function
A		
B		
C		

[6 marks]

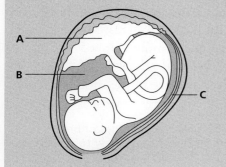

Figure 20.6

Student's answer

Part	Name	Function
A	placenta ✓	provides the fetus with blood containing oxygen from the mother ✗
B	amniotic fluid ✓	protects the fetus ✗
C	uterus ✗	contains the fetus during pregnancy ✗

Examiner's comments *The description of the function of the placenta is very badly worded: the placenta prevents the blood of the mother and fetus from mixing. Answers containing biologically incorrect information are penalised.*

Details about the amniotic fluid are too vague to gain the mark for the function. The correct answer was 'to protect the fetus from physical damage'.

*Part **C** is the amniotic sac, which contains the amniotic fluid.*

Ante-natal care

Before the baby is born, it obtains all its dietary requirements from its mother through the placenta. The mother's diet needs to be balanced so that the fetus receives all the materials needed for healthy growth and development. Amino acids are needed to form proteins for growth; calcium is needed for development of the skeleton; iron for red blood cell formation. If the mother's diet is deficient in any nutrient, the baby may not develop properly. This means that the mother needs more protein, calcium, iron, vitamin C and energy (from carbohydrates or fats) than normal in her diet. Drugs such as aspirin and heroin, along with nicotine and carbon monoxide from smoking, alcohol from drinks, and viruses such as HIV and rubella (German measles) can all pass across the placenta, risking the health of the developing fetus.

Advantages of breastfeeding over bottle-feeding

Some of the advantages are to the baby, while others are to the mother:

- there are antibodies present in breast milk, giving the baby protection against infection
- foodstuffs are present in breast milk in the correct proportions
- there is no risk of an allergic reaction to breast milk
- breast milk is produced at the correct temperature
- there are no additives or preservatives in breast milk
- breastfeeding builds a bond between mother and baby
- breast milk does not require sterilisation as there are no bacteria present that could cause intestinal disease
- there is no cost involved in using breast milk
- breast milk does not need to be prepared
- breastfeeding triggers a reduction in the size of the mother's uterus.

Examiner's tip

▶ You are unlikely to need to describe all the advantages of breast-feeding. Choose three or four from the list that are easy to remember.

Birth

- The first stage of the birth process is called labour, triggered by the hormone oxytocin.
- The muscular walls of the uterus start to contract.
- The pressure breaks the amniotic sac, releasing the amniotic fluid (this is known as the waters breaking).
- Contractions gradually become more frequent, pushing the baby down towards the cervix, which becomes dilated to allow the baby to pass through.
- The vagina stretches to allow the baby to be born.
- The baby is still attached to the placenta by the umbilical cord, so this is cut and tied.
- The placenta breaks away from the wall of the uterus and passes out (this is known as the afterbirth).

● **Try this**   The answer is given on **p. 143**.

2 Describe, in sequence, the main events which occur during birth.

[3 marks]

Sex hormones

These are responsible for the development of secondary sexual characteristics at puberty. Testosterone, secreted by the testes, causes the changes in boys; oestrogen, secreted by the ovaries, causes the changes in girls. Puberty is when the sex organs (ovaries in girls; testes in boys) become mature and start to secrete hormones as well as making gametes (ova and sperms). Puberty happens at about 10–14 years old, but varies from person to person.

The table on the facing page shows the secondary sexual characteristics that appear at puberty. A drop in hormone levels can reduce these features, while a high level of hormone can increase them.

Male	Female
Voice becomes much lower (breaks)	Breasts grow, nipples enlarge
Hair starts to grow on chest, face, under arms and in pubic area	Hair develops under arms and in pubic area
Body becomes more muscular	Hips become wider
Penis becomes larger	Uterus and vagina become larger
Testes start to produce sperm	Ovaries start to release eggs and periods begin (menstruation)

● **Try this**   The answers are given on **p. 143**.

3 Figure 20.7 represents part of the male reproductive system, together with parts of the urinary system.

   a) Copy or trace the figure and label:
     i) the sperm duct (vas deferens)   [1 mark]
     ii) the urethra.   [1 mark]

   b) What is the difference in function of the urethra in males and females?   [2 marks]

   c) **i)** The hormone testosterone controls the development of secondary sexual characteristics in males. State **two** of these characteristics which develop at puberty.   [2 marks]
     ii) On your drawing label clearly where this hormone is produced.   [1 mark]

     iii) Some international athletes, female as well as male, have taken testosterone, illegally, as a drug. Suggest why these athletes might have done this.   [2 marks]

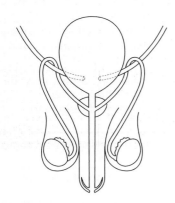

Figure 20.7

Production of oestrogen and progesterone

The sites of production of oestrogen and progesterone in the menstrual cycle and in pregnancy are listed in the table.

Hormone	Site of production	
	In the menstrual cycle	**In pregnancy**
Oestrogen	Ovaries	Placenta
Progesterone	Corpus luteum (remains of follicle in ovary after ovulation)	Placenta

Methods of birth control

There are four main groups of birth control methods: natural, chemical, mechanical and surgical. Details are given in the table on the next page.

Type	Example	Details	Comments
Natural	Withdrawal	The penis is withdrawn from the vagina before ejaculation	Very unreliable – some semen is released before ejaculation
	Abstinence	No sexual intercourse	The best way of avoiding an unwanted pregnancy
	Rhythm method	The time of ovulation is predicted and intercourse is avoided around this date	Time of ovulation can vary, so not always reliable
Chemical	Contraceptive pill	Contains progesterone and oestrogen, which prevent ovulation, or progesterone only (the 'mini-pill') – which prevents implantation of a blastula	Different strengths are available – a doctor needs to decide. Usually very reliable when taken regularly
	Spermicide	Kills sperm in the vagina	Should only be used with a condom or diaphragm
Mechanical	Condom	Rubber sheath placed over the penis to stop sperm entering the vagina	Also prevents transmission of sexually transmitted diseases; reliable if used with a spermicide
	Diaphragm	Dome-shaped rubber barrier that fits in the vagina at the cervix	Needs to be the correct size; must be left in place for 6 hours after intercourse; reliable if used with a spermicide
	Femidom	A thin plastic sheath placed inside the vagina	Also prevents transmission of sexually transmitted diseases
	Intra-uterine device (IUD)	A plastic-coated copper coil is surgically inserted into the wall of the uterus	Prevents implantation of a blastula; reliable
Surgical	Vasectomy	Sperm ducts are tied or cut, so no sperm can leave the testes	Not normally reversible; extremely reliable
	Laparotomy	Oviducts are tied or cut, so no eggs can pass down them	Not normally reversible; extremely reliable

Social aspects of artificial insemination

Artificial insemination (AI) is a way of increasing the chances of a woman having a baby when the male partner is infertile. It involves using sperm from a donor, stored in a sperm bank. The sperm are inserted into the female partner's uterus around the time of ovulation. The baby will not carry any of the genetic characteristics of the male in the relationship, and it is argued that the child has a right to know who the real father is (the sperm donor). However, many sperm donors wish to remain anonymous.

Use of hormones in fertility drugs

Fertility drugs can be used to increase the chance of pregnancy. Follicle stimulating hormone (FSH) and luteinizing hormone (LH) treatment causes multiple release of ova (eggs), increasing the chance of pregnancy.

In vitro fertilisation – if the woman has a problem with blocked oviducts, a doctor can collect the ova produced by FSH and LH treatment. Some of the ova are fertilised in a Petri dish using the male partner's sperm (the others may be stored in case the process is not successful). The early embryos produced are then inserted into the uterus to achieve pregnancy.

The treatment is quite expensive, and not always successful. Some argue that the world's population is large enough without creating more babies artificially for infertile couples.

Sexually transmitted diseases

These are diseases passed on during unprotected sexual intercourse. You need to know about **gonorrhoea** and **human immunodeficiency virus (HIV)**.

Gonorrhoea is caused by the bacterium *Neisseria gonorrhoea*. Details are shown in the table.

Signs and symptoms	Effects	Treatment
Male: • Sores on penis • Discharge of pus from penis • Pain when urinating **Female:** • Discharge of pus from vagina, but not always obvious • Often no symptoms	• Damage to urinary and reproductive organs • Sterility • Blindness in a baby born to a mother with the disease	• Antibiotic (as gonorrhoea is caused by a bacterium)

HIV may result in AIDS (acquired immune deficiency syndrome). Details are shown in the table.

Methods of transmission	Ways of preventing its spread
• Unprotected sexual intercourse with an infected person (this includes homosexuals) • Drug use involving sharing a needle used by an infected person • Transfusions of unscreened blood • Infected mother to fetus • Feeding a baby with milk from an infected mother • Use of unsterilised surgical instruments	• Use of a condom for sexual intercourse • Abstinence from sexual intercourse • Screening of blood used for transfusions • Use of sterilised needles for drug injections • Feeding a baby with bottled milk when the mother has HIV • Use of sterilised surgical instruments

● **Try this**   The answers are given on **p. 143**.

4 i)   HIV can be passed from mother to fetus through the placenta. State **two** other ways in which the virus can be passed to an uninfected person.   [2 marks]

ii)   Name **two** other harmful materials which might pass from mother to fetus through the placenta.   [2 marks]

How HIV affects the immune system

The HIV virus attacks some types of lymphocyte (white blood cells) in the bloodstream. Lymphocytes produce antibodies, which attack the antigens present on invading microbes. Some lymphocytes are stored in lymph nodes to provide protection against future infections. HIV prevents this immunity being retained, so the AIDS sufferer has no protection against diseases such as tuberculosis (TB) and pneumonia.

TOPIC 21 Inheritance

Key objectives

- To be able to define *chromosome*, *gene*, *allele*, *haploid* and *diploid nuclei*
- To be able to describe the inheritance of sex in humans
- To be able to describe mitosis and meiosis
- To be able to define *genotype*, *phenotype*, *homozygous*, *heterozygous*, *dominant* and *recessive*
- To be able to calculate and predict the results of monohybrid crosses
- To be able to explain codominance and inheritance of blood groups

Key definitions

Chromosome	A thread of DNA, made up of genes
Gene	A section of DNA, which codes for the formation of a protein controlling a specific characteristic of the organism
Allele	An alternative form of a gene. Pairs of alleles occupy the same relative positions on chromosome pairs
Haploid nucleus	A nucleus containing a single set of unpaired chromosomes, e.g. in sperm and ova (eggs). In humans the haploid number is 23
Diploid nucleus	A nucleus containing pairs of chromosomes, e.g. in somatic (body) cells. In humans the diploid number is 46
Genotype	The genetic make-up of an organism, e.g. Tt, where T and t are alleles of a gene
Phenotype	The characteristics visible in an organism, controlled by the genotype, e.g. a tall plant or a dwarf plant
Homozygous	Having a pair of identical alleles controlling the same characteristic, e.g. TT, where T = tall. The organism will be pure-breeding for that characteristic
Heterozygous	Having a pair of dissimilar alleles for a characteristic, e.g. Tt
Dominant	A gene, e.g. T, that always shows in the phenotype of an organism whether the organism is heterozygous (Tt) or homozygous (TT)
Recessive	A gene, e.g. t, that only has an effect on the phenotype when the organism is homozygous (tt)

Key ideas

Inheritance is the transmission of genetic information from one generation to the next, leading to continuity of the species and variation within it.

Chromosomes

Human cells contain 46 chromosomes, which are in pairs. Sex cells (sperm and ova) contain only 23 chromosomes. The 23 chromosomes comprise one from each pair. Each chromosome is made up of a large number of genes coding for the formation of different proteins which give us our characteristics. The gene responsible for a particular characteristic is always on the same

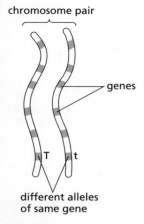

chromosome pair

genes

T   t

different alleles
of same gene

Figure 21.1

relative position on the chromosome. The Human Genome Project mapped out these positions on all 46 chromosomes (a very large task – there are 40 000 genes altogether). When the chromosomes are in pairs, there may be a different form (allele) of the gene on each chromosome – as shown in Figure 21.1.

Inheritance of sex in humans

Of the 23 pairs of chromosomes present in each human cell, one pair is the sex chromosomes. These determine the sex of the individual. Males have XY, females have XX. So the presence of a Y chromosome results in male features developing. Figure 21.2 shows how sex is inherited.

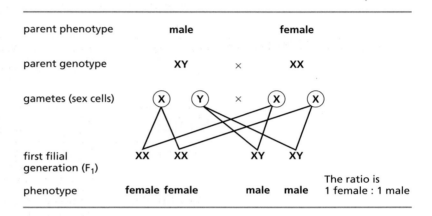

parent phenotype	**male**	**female**
parent genotype	**XY** $\times$	**XX**
gametes (sex cells)	Ⓧ Ⓨ $\times$	Ⓧ Ⓧ
first filial generation (F_1)	**XX** **XX**	**XY** **XY**
phenotype	**female** **female**	**male** **male**

The ratio is
1 female : 1 male

Figure 21.2

Mitosis and meiosis

Mitosis
Mitosis is a form of cell division used for making new cells to enable growth or the replacement of old or damaged cells. Asexual reproduction involves mitosis.

During the process, all the chromosomes are copied and split to form two nuclei with the same number of chromosomes as the parent nucleus cell (the diploid number of chromosomes is also maintained). At the end of a mitotic cell division, the number of cells is doubled and the daughter cells produced are genetically identical to the parent.

Meiosis
Sex cells are formed in the gonads (ovaries and testes) by meiosis. The gametes (sex cells) produced are haploid, but they are formed from diploid cells, so meiosis involves halving the normal chromosome number – the pairs of chromosomes are separated. At the end of the process, the cells produced are not all identical – meiosis results in variation.

When ova are formed in a woman, all the ova will carry an X chromosome. When sperm are formed in a man, half the sperm will carry an X chromosome; half will carry a Y chromosome (see Figure 21.3).

99

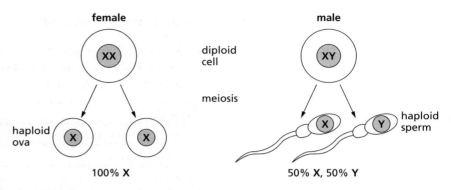

Figure 21.3 The formation of sex cells by meiosis

Examiner's tip

► Although many textbooks show the stages of mitosis and meiosis, you do not need those details for the Cambridge IGCSE exam.

Sample question and answer

Sample question Complete the following passage, using only words from the list below.

diploid   gametes   haploid   meiosis   mitosis   red blood cells

The transfer of inherited characteristics to new cells and new individuals depends on two types of cell division. During _____ , the chromosomes are duplicated exactly and _____ cells are produced.

However, during _____ , the chromosome sets are first duplicated and then halved, producing cells. These cells will become _____.   [4 marks]

Student's answer During **meiotosis ✗**, the chromosomes are duplicated exactly and **identical ✗** cells are produced.

However, during **meiosis ✓**, the chromosome sets are first duplicated and then halved, producing cells. These cells will become **gametes**. ✓

Examiner's comments *The first answer is not clear – it mixes up the terms 'mitosis' and 'meiosis'. Sometimes candidates do this deliberately when they are not sure of the answer, hoping that the examiner will give them the benefit of the doubt. (We don't!) This candidate has not followed the rubric (instructions) in the question for the second answer: the term 'identical' does not appear in the word list. The correct answers are 'mitosis' and 'diploid'.*

● **Try this** The answers are given on **p. 143**.

1 **a)** The nuclei of human liver cells contain 46 chromosomes. Copy and complete the table below to show how many chromosomes would be present in the cells listed. [3 marks]

Type of cell	Number of chromosomes
Ciliated cell in windpipe	
Red blood cell	
Ovum	

b) Describe **two** differences, other than the number of chromosomes, between nuclei produced by mitosis and those produced by meiosis.

[2 marks]

Monohybrid inheritance

This involves the study of how a single gene is passed on from parents to offspring. It is probably easiest to predict the outcome of a monohybrid cross using a punnett square (see Figure 21.4). However, if you have been taught the traditional way of displaying the cross (as shown in Figure 21.2), there is nothing wrong with using that method.

All the genetic crosses shown will involve examples using pea plants, which can be tall (T) or dwarf (t) — tall is dominant to dwarf.

Examiner's tips
▶ When you write out a genetic cross, make sure you state what the symbols represent, e.g. T = tall, t = dwarf.
▶ Make sure you label each line in the cross (phenotype, genotype, etc.).
▶ It's a good idea to circle the gametes to show that meiosis has happened.
▶ Read the question really carefully — are you asked to state the outcome in terms of the genotype or the phenotype?

A cross between a pure-breeding tall pea plant and a pure-breeding dwarf pea plant

As tall is dominant to dwarf, and both plants are pure-breeding, their genotypes must be TT and tt.

phenotypes of parents	**tall**		**dwarf**
genotypes of parents	**TT**	×	**tt**
gametes	(T) (T)	×	(t) (t)

punnett square

	(T)	(T)
(t)	**Tt**	**Tt**
(t)	**Tt**	**Tt**

F₁ genotypes   **all Tt**

F₁ phenotypes   **all tall**

Figure 21.4

A cross between two heterozygous tall pea plants

The genotype of both plants must be Tt.

phenotypes of parents	**tall**		**dwarf**	
genotypes of parents	**Tt**	×	**Tt**	
gametes	(T) (t)	×	(T) (t)	

punnett square

	T	**t**
T	**TT**	**Tt**
t	**Tt**	**tt**

F$_1$ genotypes	**1 TT, 2 Tt, 1 tt**
F$_1$ phenotypes	**tall tall dwarf**
ratio	3 tall : 1 dwarf

Figure 21.5

A cross between a heterozygous tall pea plant and a dwarf pea plant

The heterozygous tall pea plant must be Tt. The dwarf pea plant must be tt.

phenotypes of parents	**tall**		**dwarf**	
genotypes of parents	**Tt**	×	**tt**	
gametes	(T) (t)	×	(t) (t)	

punnett square

	T	**t**
t	**Tt**	**tt**
t	**Tt**	**tt**

F$_1$ genotypes	**2 Tt, 2 tt**
F$_1$ phenotypes	**tall dwarf**
ratio	1 tall : 1 dwarf

Figure 21.6

Common misconceptions

Some students ignore the letters for alleles given in genetic questions and make up their own, without stating a key. This usually results in a number of marks being lost through errors that could easily have been avoided. ■

● **Try this**   The answers are given on **pp. 143–4**.

2 In exam questions involving genetic crosses, you often need to predict the genotypes of the parents from descriptions of them. Work out the following genotypes, based on peas that can be round or wrinkled, with round being dominant to wrinkled. Remember that the dominant allele normally takes the capital letter of the characteristic it represents.

   a) A heterozygous round pea   [1 mark]
   b) A wrinkled pea   [1 mark]
   c) A pure-breeding round pea   [1 mark]

3 Copy and complete the passage by writing the most appropriate word from the list in each space.

   chromosome   diploid   gene   heterozygous   meiosis

   mutation   phenotype   recessive   dominant

   Petal colour in pea plants is controlled by a single _____ which has two forms, red and white. The pollen grains are produced by _____ . After pollination, fertilisation occurs and the gametes join to form a _____ zygote.

   When two red-flowered pea plants were crossed with each other, some of the offspring were white-flowered. The _____ of the rest of the offspring was red-flowered. The white-flowered form is _____ to the red-flowered form and each of the parent plants was therefore _____ .   [6 marks]

Codominance

This term describes a pair of alleles, neither of which is dominant over the other. This means both can have an effect on the phenotype when they are present together in the genotype. The result is that there can be three different phenotypes. When writing the genotypes of codominant alleles, the common convention is to use a capital letter to represent the gene involved, and a small raised (superscript) letter for each phenotype.

Example: with the gene for flower colour in a plant, the alleles are C^R (red) and C^W (white). The capital letter **C** has been chosen to represent **colour**. Pure-breeding (homozygous) flowers may be red ($C^R C^R$) or white ($C^W C^W$). If these are cross–pollinated, all the first filial generation will be heterozygous ($C^R C^W$), and they are pink because both alleles have an effect on the phenotype.

Self-pollinating the pink (F_1) plants results in an unusual ratio in the next (F_2) generation of 1 red : 2 pink : 1 white.

● **Try this**   The answers are given on **p. 144**.

4 Write out a genetic cross for the example described above, to prove that the ratio achieved is 1 : 2 : 1. Use the same layout as in the examples given earlier.   [6 marks]

Common misconceptions

When factors are codominant, students often think this will result in different proportions of offspring having the parents' features. However, codominance results in the appearance of a new characteristic, which is intermediate to the parents' features. For example, if the parents are pure-breeding for long fur and short fur, the offspring will all have medium-length fur. ■

Inheritance of A, B, AB and O blood groups

These blood groups give an example of codominance. Instead of two alleles being present, in this case there are three – I^A, I^B and I^O. Combinations of these can result in four different phenotypes – A, B, AB and O. The alleles are responsible for producing antigens that respond to foreign antibodies (this can result in blood clotting in blood transfusions, and rejection of organs after transplant operations). However, while I^A and I^B are codominant, I^O is dominated by both the other alleles. This means, for example, that a person with blood group A could have the genotype I^AI^A or I^AI^O. This has implications when having children because, if both parents carry the I^O allele, a child could be born with the genotype I^OI^O (blood group O), even though neither of the parents have this phenotype.

Example: inheritance of blood group O

Two parents have blood groups A and B. The father is I^AI^O and the mother is I^BI^O.

phenotypes of parents	blood group A		blood group B
genotypes of parents	I^AI^O	×	I^BI^O
gametes	I^A I^O	×	I^B I^O

punnett square

	I^A	I^O
I^B	I^AI^B	I^BI^O
I^O	I^AI^O	I^OI^O

F_1 genotypes	I^AI^O, I^BI^O, I^AI^B, I^OI^O
F_1 phenotypes	A B AB O
ratio	1 : 1 : 1 : 1

Figure 21.7

TOPIC 22 Variation

Key objectives

- To be able to describe continuous and discontinuous variation
- To be able to define *mutation* and outline its causes
- To be able to describe the production of varieties of animals and plants by artificial selection
- To be able to define *natural selection*
- To be able to define *genetic engineering*
- To be able to describe sickle cell anaemia, and explain its incidence in relation to that of malaria
- To be able to describe variation and the role of competition in natural selection
- To be able to assess the importance of natural selection as a possible mechanism for evolution
- To be able to describe the development of strains of antibiotic-resistant bacteria
- To be able to explain why, and outline how human insulin genes were put into bacteria using genetic engineering

Key definitions

Mutation	A spontaneous change in a gene or a chromosome. It can be caused during the copying of DNA, or by exposure to radiation or some chemicals
Natural selection	Passing on of genes to the next generation by the best-adapted organisms, without human interference
Genetic engineering	Taking a gene from one species and putting it into another species

Key ideas

Variation

There are two main types of variation – continuous and discontinuous.

Continuous variation

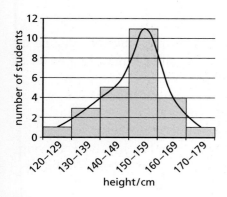

Figure 22.1

Continuous variation shows a complete range of the characteristic within a population. It is caused both by genes (often a number of different genes) and by the environment. Environmental influences for plants may be the availability of, or competition for, nutrients, light, water and exposure to disease. For animals, it may be availability of food or balanced diet, exposure to disease (or the availability of health services for humans), etc.

Examples of continuous variation include height, body mass and intelligence. When the frequency is plotted on a graph as in Figure 22.1, a smooth curve is produced, with the majority of the population sample grouped together and only small numbers at the extremes of the graph.

Discontinuous variation

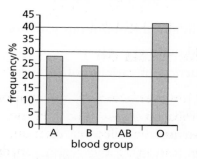

Figure 22.2 Blood groups in a population

Discontinuous variation is seen where there are obvious, distinct categories for a feature. There are no intermediates between categories, and the feature cannot usually change during life. It is caused by a single gene or a small number of genes, with no environmental influence (as in Figure 22.2).

Examples include blood group, ability to tongue-roll and earlobe shape. When the frequencies are plotted on a graph, bars are produced which cannot be linked with a smooth curve.

> **Examiner's tip**
> ▶ For this syllabus, you do not need to explain which combinations of blood groups are safe to mix during transfusions.

● **Try this**   The answers are given on **p. 144**.

1 Seventy seeds were collected from a cross between two plants of the same species. The seeds were sown at the same time and, after 3 weeks, the heights of the plants which grew were measured and found to fall into two groups, **A** and **B**, as shown in Figure 22.3.

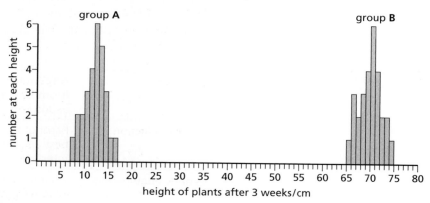

Figure 22.3

a) Calculate the percentage of seeds which germinated. Show your working. [2 marks]

b) i) Name the type of variation shown **within each group**. [1 mark]
   ii) State **three** factors which might have caused this variation. [3 marks]

Mutation

This is a source of variation, caused by an unpredictable change in the genes or chromosome numbers. The change may be a result of faulty copying when DNA is replicated, faulty separation of chromosomes during cell division, or exposure to radiation or some chemicals.

Down's syndrome is caused by a mutation. When ova are formed in the ovaries, the chromosome number is halved. During this division process (meiosis), one of the chromosomes (number 23) sticks to its partner. This results in one ovum with 24 chromosomes and one with only 22, and the ovum with 24 chromosomes is still viable. If it is fertilised, the fetus formed will have 47 chromosomes instead of 46. The presence of the extra chromosome causes unusual characteristics in the baby. These usually include lowered life expectancy, mental retardation (although some Down's children are very intelligent), early puberty, and a distinctive round face and short neck.

Effects of radiation and chemicals on mutation rate

Mutations are normally very rare. However, exposure to radiation and some chemicals, such as tar in tobacco smoke, increases the rate of mutation. Exposure can cause uncontrolled cell division, leading to the formation of tumours (cancer). Exposure of gonads (testes and ovaries) to radiation can lead to sterility or to damage to genes in sex cells that can be passed on to children. Some scientists argue that there is a higher incidence of leukaemia (a form of white blood cell cancer) in the children of workers at nuclear power stations.

Sickle cell anaemia and its incidence in relation to that of malaria

Sickle cell anaemia is caused by a mutation in the blood pigment haemoglobin. When the faulty haemoglobin is present in a red blood cell, it causes the cell to deform and become sickle-shaped, especially when oxygen levels in the blood become low. In this state the sickled red blood cells are less efficient at transporting oxygen and more likely to become stuck in a capillary, preventing blood flow.

The faulty allele is dominated by the allele for normal haemoglobin, but still has some effect in a heterozygous genotype. The possible genotypes are:

- $H^N H^N$ normal haemoglobin, no anaemia
- $H^N H^n$ some abnormal haemoglobin, sickle cell trait (not life-threatening)
- $H^n H^n$ abnormal haemoglobin, sickle cell anaemia (life-threatening).

Malaria is a life-threatening disease caused by a parasite that invades red blood cells. The parasite is carried by some species of mosquito. However, a person who is heterozygous ($H^N H^n$) for sickle cell anaemia has protection from malaria, because the malaria parasite is unable to invade and reproduce in the sickle cells. A person who is homozygous for sickle cell anaemia ($H^n H^n$) also has protection, but is at high risk of dying from sickle cell anaemia. A person with normal haemoglobin ($H^N H^N$) in a malarial country is at high risk of contracting malaria.

When the distributions of malaria and sickle cell anaemia are shown on a map of the world, it is found that the two coincide in tropical areas because of the selective advantage of the H^n allele in providing protection against malaria.

Selection

Artificial selection is used by humans to produce varieties of animals and plants that have an increased economic importance.

Examples
- A variety of cattle may have a higher than average milk yield. Another variety may have a very high meat yield. If the two varieties are cross-bred, a new breed could be artificially produced that has the benefits of both parental varieties (high milk production in females; high meat yield in males).
- Wild varieties of plants sometimes have increased resistance to fungal diseases, but have poor fruit yield. Cross-breeding wheat plants can result in the formation of varieties that have both high resistance to disease and high seed yield.

● **Try this**   The answers are given on **p. 144**.

2 Farmers have carried out artificial selection to improve the breeds of some animals. Some of the original breeds have become very rare and are in danger of becoming extinct.

   a) Explain what is meant by artificial selection.   [2 marks]

   b) i)   Name **one** species which is in danger of extinction.   [1 mark]

       ii) Biologists are concerned that species of animals and plants should not become extinct. Why is it important to prevent the extinction of plant and animal species?   [2 marks]

Variation describes differences in a population. Some variation is inherited (passed on from parents) and some is acquired (developed during life).

Animals and plants produced by sexual reproduction will show variation from their parents, for example in the size of the muscles in the legs of lions. When new organisms are produced, not all of them are likely to survive because of competition for resources such as food, water and shelter. The same is true for plants (they compete for resources such as nutrients, light, water and space). The individuals with the most favourable characteristics are most likely to survive. The process of natural selection follows a sequence, as listed below.

- Some of the variations within a population may give some individuals an advantage over others in the population. Bigger muscles in the legs of a lion would enable it to run more quickly and get food more successfully.
- In an environment where there is a food shortage, the lion with the biggest leg muscles is most likely to survive to adulthood.
- The weaker individuals die before having the chance to breed, but the surviving adults breed and pass on the advantageous genes to their offspring.
- More of the next generation carry the advantageous genes, resulting in a stronger population, better adapted to a changing environment.

Slow changes in the environment result in adaptations in a population to cope with the change. Failure to adapt could result in the species becoming extinct. This gradual change in the species through natural selection over time, in response to changes in the environment, is a possible mechanism for evolution.

Example: antibiotic-resistant strains of bacteria

Bacteria reproduce rapidly – a new generation can be produced every 20 minutes by binary fission (see page 82). Antibiotics are used to treat bacterial infections: an antibiotic is a chemical that kills bacteria by preventing bacterial cell wall formation. Mutations occur during reproduction, which produce some variation in the population of bacteria. Individual bacteria with the most favourable features are most likely to survive and reproduce. A mutation may occur that enables a bacterium to resist being killed by antibiotic treatment, while the rest of the population is killed when treated. This bacterium would survive the treatment and breed, passing on the antibiotic-resistant gene to its offspring. Future treatment of this population of bacteria using the antibiotic would be ineffective.

Genetic engineering

This is a process by which a gene is taken from a chromosome of one species and put into the chromosome of another species.

Using genetic engineering to put human insulin genes into bacteria

Figure 22.4 on the next page shows this process. The steps are numbered on the diagram as in the list below.

1 Human cells with genes for healthy insulin are selected.
2 A chromosome (which is a length of DNA) is removed from the cell.
3 The insulin gene is cut from the chromosome using restriction endonuclease enzyme.
4 A suitable bacterial cell is selected. Some of its DNA is in the form of circular plasmids.
5 All the plasmids are removed from the bacterial cell.
6 The plasmids are cut open using the same restriction endonuclease enzyme.
7 The human insulin gene is inserted into the plasmids using ligase enzyme.
8 The plasmids are returned to the bacterial cell (only one is shown in the diagram).
9 The bacterial cell is allowed to reproduce in a fermenter. All the cells produced contain plasmids with the human insulin gene.

continued

The importance of this process

- Diabetics need a source of insulin to control their blood sugar levels. In the past cow insulin has been used, but some people are allergic to it. Human insulin produced from genetically engineered bacteria will not trigger an allergic reaction.
- The insulin is acceptable to people with a range of religious beliefs who may not be allowed to use insulin from animals such as cows or pigs.
- The product is very pure.
- Human insulin can be made on a commercial scale, reducing costs.

Figure 22.4

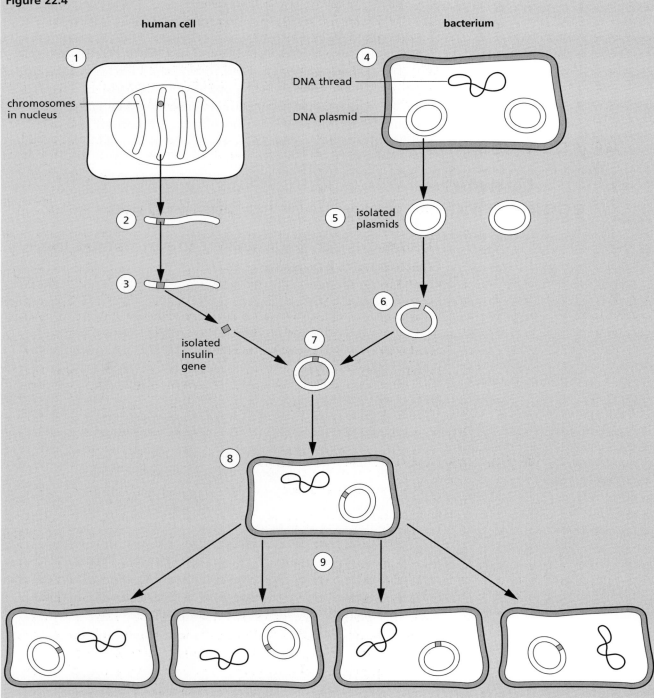

TOPIC 23 Energy flow, food chains and food webs

Key objectives
- To be able to state the role of the Sun in biological systems
- To be able to describe the non-cyclical nature of energy flow
- To be able to define the terms *food chain*, *food web*, *producer*, *consumer*, *herbivore*, *carnivore*, *decomposer*, *ecosystem* and *trophic level*
- To be able to describe energy losses between trophic levels, and the advantages of short food chains
- To be able to describe and interpret pyramids of numbers, biomass and energy
- To be able to recognise the increased efficiency of using green plants as human food, compared with eating animals that have been fed on crop plants

Key definitions

Carnivore	An animal that eats other animals
Consumer	An organism that obtains its food by feeding on other organisms
Decomposer	An organism that obtains its food by breaking down dead organisms
Ecosystem	A community of interdependent organisms and their environment
Food chain	A list of organisms that shows the feeding relationship between them and the direction of energy flow
Food web	A group of interlinking food chains that shows the feeding relationships between organisms
Herbivore	An animal that eats plants
Producer	An organism that makes its own food using energy from sunlight through the process of photosynthesis
Trophic level	An organism's position in a food chain, food web or food pyramid

● **Try this** The answers are given on **p. 144**.

1 State the difference between the terms in each of the following pairs:

   a) *producer* and *consumer* [4 marks]

   b) *carnivore* and *herbivore*. [2 marks]

Key ideas ## Energy flow

The Sun is the principal source of energy input to biological systems. The Earth receives two main types of energy from the Sun: light (solar) and heat. Photosynthetic plants and some bacteria can trap light energy and convert it into chemical energy. Heterotrophic organisms obtain their energy by eating plants or animals that have eaten plants. So all organisms, directly or indirectly, get their energy from the Sun. The energy is passed from one organism to another in a food chain but, unlike water and elements such as carbon and nitrogen, energy does not return in a cycle. Energy given out by organisms is lost to the environment.

Food chains

These are lists of organisms that show the feeding relationship between them, as in the example below.

maize $\rightarrow$ locust $\rightarrow$ lizard $\rightarrow$ snake

producer   primary consumer   secondary consumer   tertiary consumer

> ### Examiner's tip
> ▶ When writing out a food chain, don't include the Sun (it is not an organism).

A food chain usually starts with a photosynthetic plant, which gains its energy from the Sun. The arrows used to link each organism to the next represent the direction of energy flow. They always point towards the 'eater', and away from the plant. The feeding level is known as the **trophic level**.

- Plants are producers (they make – or produce – food for other organisms).
- Animals that eat plants are primary consumers (a consumer is an 'eater'). They are also called herbivores.
- Animals that eat other animals are secondary, or possibly tertiary, consumers depending on their position in the chain. They are also called carnivores.

> ### Examiner's tips
> ▶ Make sure you can write a food chain involving three consumers, with the arrows in the correct direction.
> ▶ Always start with the producer on the left of the diagram.
> ▶ Practice labelling each trophic level in your food chain under the organisms (producer, primary consumer, etc.).
> ▶ Don't waste time drawing the plants and animals: this will not get you any extra marks.

Energy is lost at each level in the food chain, as in the examples below.

- Energy lost through the process of respiration (as heat).
- Energy used up for movement (to search for food, find a mate, escape from predators, etc.).
- Warm-blooded animals (birds and mammals) maintain a constant body temperature – they lose heat to the environment.
- Warm-blooded animals lose heat energy in faeces and urine.
- Some of the material in the organism being eaten is not used by the consumer, for example a locust does not eat the roots of maize, and some of the parts eaten are not digestible.

Even plants do not make use of all the light energy available to them. This is because some light:

- is reflected off shiny leaves
- is the wrong wavelength for chlorophyll to trap
- passes through the leaves without passing through any chloroplasts
- does not fall on the leaves.

On average, about 90% of the energy is lost at each level in a food chain. This means that in long food chains, very little of the energy entering the chain through the producer is available to the top carnivore. So there tend to be small numbers of top carnivores. The food chain below shows how energy reduces through the chain. It is based on maize obtaining 100 units of energy.

maize $\longrightarrow$ locust $\longrightarrow$ lizard $\longrightarrow$ snake

100 units   10 units   1 unit   0.1 unit

In shorter food chains, less energy is lost.

Examiner's tip
▶ When describing food chains, food webs and pyramids, try to use the terms defined at the start of this topic wherever possible. Answers containing correct terminology used appropriately are more likely to earn you high marks.

● **Try this**   The answers are given on **p. 144**.

2 Figure 23.1 shows the flow of energy through a complete food chain.

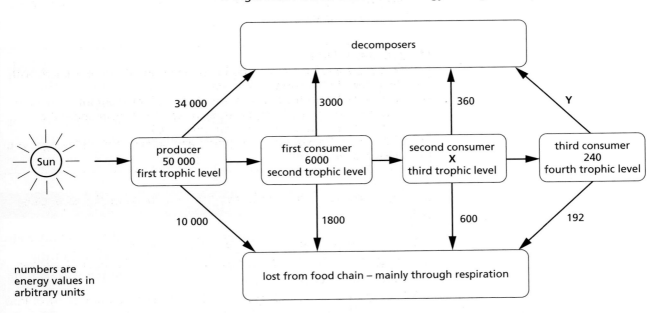

numbers are energy values in arbitrary units

Figure 23.1

a) i) Which form of the Sun's energy is trapped by the producer?

[1 mark]

ii) Into which energy form is the Sun's energy converted when it is trapped by the producer?   [1 mark]

continued

b) i) The first consumer has received 6000 units of energy. How many units of energy (**X** on the figure) have been passed to the second consumer? [1 mark]

ii) How many units of energy (**Y** on the figure) are lost from the third consumer to the decomposers? [1 mark]

c) i) Suggest why the proportion of the energy intake which a producer loses to the environment (20%) is smaller than that lost to the environment by a first consumer (30%). [2 marks]

ii) Many countries have difficulty in producing enough food for their population. How might it help to overcome this problem if humans were always fed as first consumers, rather than second or third consumers? [3 marks]

Food webs

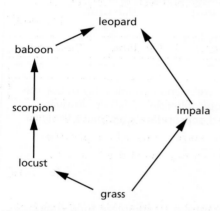

Figure 23.2

These are a more accurate way of showing feeding relationships than food chains, because most animals have more than one food source. For example, in the food web in Figure 23.2, the leopard feeds on baboons and impala. Note that the leopard can be placed at two different trophic levels: as a secondary consumer (feeding on impala); and as a quaternary or fourth level consumer (feeding on baboons).

Food webs are easily unbalanced, especially if one population of organisms in the web dies or disappears. This may happen for a number of reasons, including:

- over-predation or hunting
- disease
- pollution
- use of pesticides
- lack of food (or other resources)
- emigration.

For example, in the food web here, if all the baboons were killed by hunters the leopard would have only impala to eat. So the impala population would decrease. The scorpion population may increase because of less predation by baboons, but if there are more scorpions they will eat more locusts, reducing the locust population, and so on.

Common misconceptions

Marks are often lost when students write out food chains and webs because they draw the arrows the wrong way round or put the chain back-to-front (or both). The following example was seen in a recent paper:

jackal → sheep → grass

This student is suggesting that grass eats sheep and sheep eat jackals! ■

● **Try this** The answers are given on **p. 144**.

3 Figure 23.3 shows a food web.

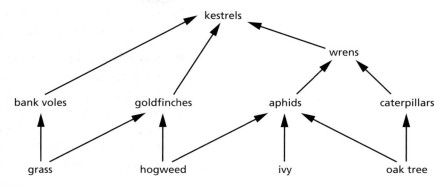

Figure 23.3

a) Select appropriate organisms from the food web to complete each column in the table below. [4 marks]

	Consumer	Producer	Carnivore	Herbivore
Organism 1				
Organism 2				

b) Ladybirds eat aphids. A very large number of ladybirds arrive in the habitat where these organisms live. Predict some of the possible effects this could have on the organisms in the above food web.

[6 marks]

Food pyramids

In a food pyramid, each trophic level in a food chain is represented by a horizontal bar, with the width of the bar representing the number of organisms, the amount of biomass or the amount of energy available at that level. The base of the pyramid represents the producer; the second level is the primary consumer; and so on.

Pyramids of numbers

Figure 23.4 shows a typical pyramid of numbers.

Usually the producers have the largest numbers, so they form the widest bar. There will be fewer primary consumers, and fewest secondary consumers, so a pyramid shape is formed. However, this is not always true. Figure 23.5 shows a different pyramid of numbers.

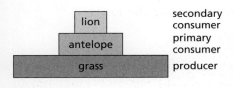

Figure 23.4

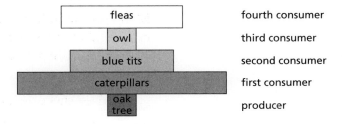

Figure 23.5

This food chain is supported by a single organism (a large oak tree). Many caterpillars feed on its leaves. Only a single owl is supported by the blue tits. However, the owl has many fleas, which feed on it by sucking its blood.

Pyramids of biomass

Figure 23.5 shows that pyramids of number are limited in what they show. It is more useful to measure the amount of living material (biomass) at each level over a fixed area of habitat. Once this is done, a normal-shaped pyramid is usually obtained, as shown in Figure 23.6.

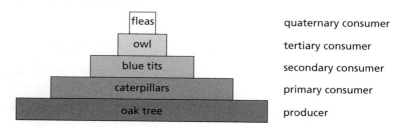

fleas	quaternary consumer
owl	tertiary consumer
blue tits	secondary consumer
caterpillars	primary consumer
oak tree	producer

Figure 23.6

Pyramids of energy

These are constructed by measuring the amount of energy available at each level in the food chain. The energy is measured over a fixed period of time. A normal-shaped pyramid is always produced because there is a reduced amount of energy at each successive level. The process of collecting data for pyramids of energy is destructive because the organisms have to be killed and burned to measure their energy content.

Food chains and energy

In terms of conservation of energy, short food chains are more efficient than long ones in providing energy to the top consumer. Below are two food chains and energy values for each level in them. Both food chains have a human being as the top consumer.

maize $\rightarrow$ cow $\rightarrow$ human

units of energy   100   10   1

maize $\rightarrow$ human

units of energy   100   10

Ten times more energy is available to the human in the second food chain than in the first. In the second food chain, the human is a herbivore (vegetarian). But eating parts of a cow provides humans with other nutrients, as well as those we gain energy from – it would be very difficult to persuade everyone to become vegetarian for the sake of energy efficiency.

Some farmers try to maximise meat production by reducing movement of their animals (keeping them in pens or cages with a food supply) and keeping them warm in winter. This means less stored energy is wasted by the animals.

TOPIC 24 Nutrient cycles

Key objectives
- To be able to describe the carbon and water cycles
- To be able to describe the nitrogen cycle
- To be able to discuss the effects of burning fossil fuels and cutting down forests on the balance between oxygen and carbon dioxide

Key ideas The carbon cycle

Figure 24.1 shows the main parts of the carbon cycle.

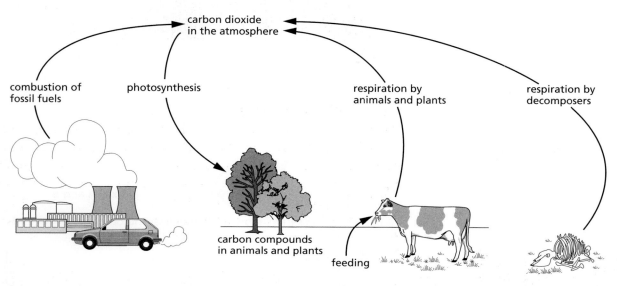

Figure 24.1

- Carbon moves into and out of the atmosphere mainly in the form of carbon dioxide.
- Plants take carbon dioxide out of the air by photosynthesis.
- Plants convert carbon dioxide into organic materials (carbohydrates, fats and proteins).
- Herbivores obtain carbon compounds by eating plants. Carnivores gain carbon compounds by eating other animals.
- Animals and plants release carbon dioxide back into the air through respiration.
- When organisms die they usually rot (decompose). Decomposers break down the organic molecules through the process of respiration, to release energy. This also releases carbon dioxide into the air.
- If a dead organism does not decompose, the carbon compounds are trapped in its body. Over a long period this can form fossil fuels such as coal, oil or gas.
- Combustion of fossil fuels releases carbon dioxide back into the air.

Examiner's tips
▶ Don't be put off by complicated diagrams of the carbon cycle. Four main processes are involved: photosynthesis, respiration, decomposition and combustion.
▶ Study the word equations for respiration and photosynthesis: they are basically the same, but reversed.

● **Try this** The answers are given on **p. 144**.

1 Figure 24.2 shows a diagram of the carbon cycle.

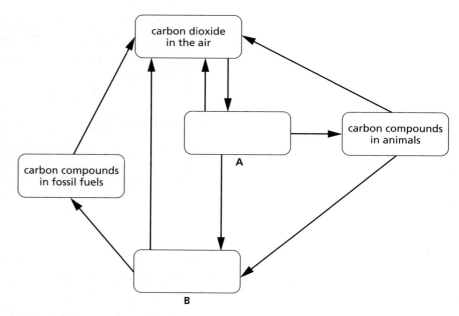

Figure 24.2

a) Copy and complete the cycle by filling in boxes **A** and **B**.   [2 marks]

b) On your diagram, label with the letter indicated an arrow that represents the process of:
   i)   combustion – **C**   [1 mark]
   ii) decomposition – **D**   [1 mark]
   iii) photosynthesis – **P**   [1 mark]
   iv) respiration – **R**   [1 mark]

Common misconceptions

Plants do not start respiring when they stop photosynthesising (at night) – they respire all the time, but during the day there is usually a net intake of carbon dioxide and output of oxygen. ■

The water cycle

Figure 24.3 shows the main parts of the water cycle.

- Plants release water vapour into the air through transpiration.
- Water evaporates from seas, lakes, rivers and soil.
- Water vapour condenses in the air, forming clouds.
- Water returns to the land as rain (precipitation), draining into streams, rivers, lakes and seas.
- Plant roots take up water by osmosis.
- In addition, animals lose water to the environment through exhaling and sweating, and in urine and faeces.

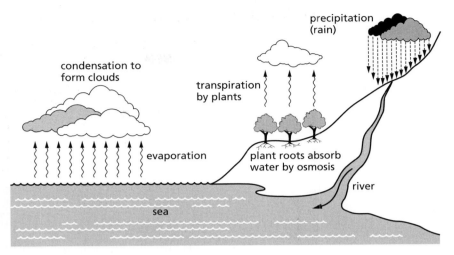

Figure 24.3

The nitrogen cycle

Figure 24.4 shows the main parts of the nitrogen cycle. You do not need to know the names of individual bacteria, but you do need to know the roles of the three main types:

- **nitrogen-fixing bacteria** – convert nitrogen gas into compounds of ammonia
- **nitrifying bacteria** – convert compounds of ammonia into nitrates
- **denitrifying bacteria** – break down nitrites into nitrogen gas.

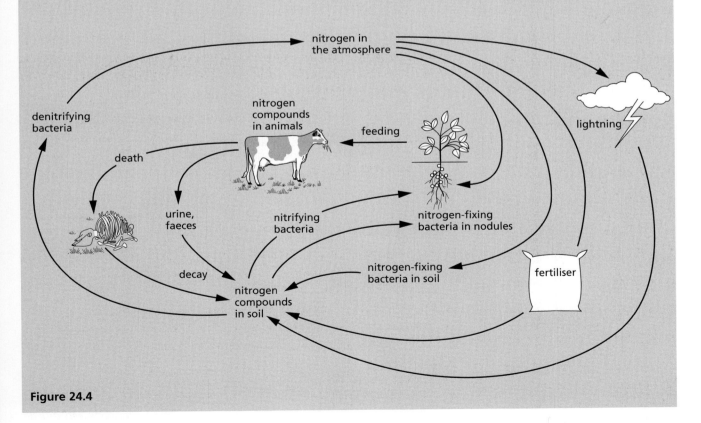

Figure 24.4

119

The element nitrogen is a very unreactive gas. Plants are not able to change it into nitrogen compounds, but it is needed to form proteins. Nitrogen compounds become available for plants in the soil in a number of ways, including:

- nitrogen-fixing bacteria (some plants – legumes such as peas, beans and clover – have roots with nodules that contain these bacteria, so the plant receives a direct source of nitrates)
- breakdown of dead plants and animals by decomposers (bacteria, fungi and invertebrates)
- the addition of artificial fertilisers, compost (decaying plant material) and manure (decaying animal waste – urine and faeces)
- lightning – its energy causes nitrogen to react with oxygen.

Plants absorb nitrates into their roots by active uptake (see Topic 6). The nitrates are combined with glucose (from photosynthesis) to form proteins. Proteins are passed through the food chain as animals eat the plants. When animals digest proteins the amino acids released can be reorganised to form different proteins.

Some soil bacteria – denitrifying bacteria – break down nitrogen compounds and release nitrogen back into the atmosphere. This is a destructive process, commonly occurring in waterlogged soil. Farmers try to keep soil well drained to prevent this happening – a shortage of nitrates in the soil stunts the growth of crop plants.

Nitrates and other ammonium compounds are very soluble, so they are easily leached out of the soil and can cause pollution (see Topic 26).

Farmers can increase the fertility (nitrogen compound concentration) of their soil by:

- adding artificial fertilisers
- adding manure or compost
- growing leguminous plants, then ploughing the roots (with their nodules) into the soil.

● **Try this**   The answers are given on **p. 145**.

2 Figure 24.5 shows the nitrogen cycle.

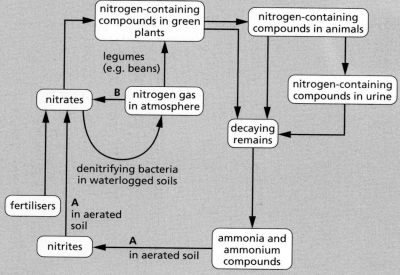

Figure 24.5

continued

a) i) Name the main nitrogen-containing compound found both in plants and in animals. [1 mark]

   ii) Name one nitrogen-containing compound that is present in urine. [1 mark]

   iii) Name the type of organism that causes the changes at **A**. [1 mark]

   iv) What atmospheric conditions bring about the change at **B**? [1 mark]

b) Using the figure, explain why it is an advantage to have good drainage in most agricultural land. [4 marks]

Balance between oxygen and carbon dioxide

Photosynthesis takes carbon dioxide out of the atmosphere and replaces it with oxygen. Respiration and combustion both do the opposite: they use up oxygen and replace it with carbon dioxide. The equations are essentially the same, but reversed:

$$\text{carbon dioxide} + \text{water} \underset{\text{respiration, combustion}}{\overset{\text{photosynthesis}}{\rightleftharpoons}} \text{glucose} + \text{oxygen}$$

In order for the amount of carbon dioxide in the atmosphere to remain stable, the rates of these processes need to be balanced. Processes that change the equilibrium (balance) include:

- cutting down forests (deforestation) – less photosynthesis
- combustion of fossil fuels (coal, oil and gas)
- increasing numbers of animals (including humans) – they all respire.

An increase in carbon dioxide levels in the atmosphere is thought to contribute to global warming. Carbon dioxide forms a layer in the atmosphere, which traps heat radiation from the Sun. This causes a gradual increase in the atmospheric temperature which can:

- melt polar ice caps, causing flooding of low-lying land
- change weather conditions in some countries, increasing flooding or reducing rainfall and changing arable (farm) land to desert
- cause the extinction of some species that cannot survive at higher temperatures.

121

TOPIC 25 Population size

Key objectives

- To be able to state the factors affecting the rate of population growth, and describe their importance
- To be able to identify the phases of a sigmoid curve of population growth
- To be able to describe the increase in population size in the absence of limiting factors, and the social implications of the current human survival rate
- To be able to interpret graphs and diagrams of human population growth
- To be able to explain the factors that lead to each of the phases in a sigmoid curve of population growth

Key ideas

Factors affecting the rate of population growth, and their importance

A population is a group of one species of organism, living in the same place. The rate of growth of a population depends on the following.

- **Food supply** – ample food will enable organisms to breed more successfully to produce more offspring; shortage of food can result in death or force emigration, reducing the population.
- **Predation** – if there is heavy predation of a population, the breeding rate may not be sufficient to produce enough organisms to replace those eaten, so the population will drop in numbers. There tends to be a time lag in population size change for predators and their prey: as predator numbers increase, prey numbers drop; and as predator numbers drop, prey numbers rise again (unless there are other limiting factors).
- **Disease** – this is a particular problem in large populations, because disease can spread easily from one individual to another. Epidemics can reduce population sizes very rapidly.
- Use of **contraceptives** (for humans).

Effect of a limiting factor on population growth

When a limiting factor influences population growth, a sigmoid (S-shaped) curve is created, as shown in Figure 25.1 for a colony of yeast.

You need to be able to place the terms *lag*, *log*, *stationary* and *death phase* on a graph of population growth. A limiting factor such as food takes effect as the population becomes too large for supplies to be sufficient. The population growth rate reduces until births and deaths are equal. At this point there is no increase in numbers – the graph forms a plateau. As food runs out, more organisms die than are born, so the number in the population drops. This is the death phase.

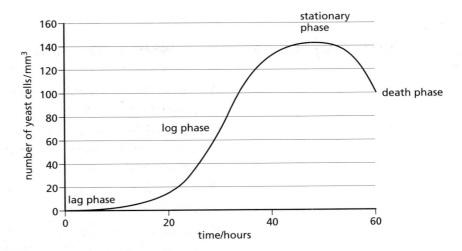

Figure 25.1

Population growth in the absence of limiting factors

If there are no limiting factors, there will be no stationary or death phase – the log phase will continue upwards, instead of the line levelling off. This has happened with human population growth. Human population size has increased exponentially because of improvements in food supply and the development of medicine to control diseases. Infant mortality has decreased, while life expectancy has increased. Such a rapid increase in population size has social implications. These include increasing demands for basic resources including food, water, space, medical care and fossil fuels. The presence of a larger human population creates greater pressures on the environment (more land needed for housing, growing crops, road building, as well as wood for fuel and housing) and, potentially, more pollution. The presence of a larger population of young people results in greater demands on education, while more old people results in greater demands on healthcare.

Graphs showing profiles of the human population in developing and developed regions of the world are not the same.

Abundant food supplies can lead to more people becoming obese: this results in greater demands on healthcare due to increasing numbers of sufferers of heart disease, diabetes, blindness, etc. In the long term this may reduce average life expectancy, as poor health becomes a limiting factor.

You need to be able to explain the factors that lead to the different phases shown in Figure 25.1 on the previous page.

- **Lag phase** – the new population takes time to settle and mature before breeding begins. When this happens, a doubling of small numbers does not have a big impact on the total population size, so the line of the graph rises only slowly with time.
- **Log (exponential) phase** – there are no limiting factors. Rapid breeding in an increasing population causes a significant increase in numbers. A steady doubling in numbers per unit of time produces a straight line.
- **Stationary phase** – limiting factors, such as shortage of food, cause the rate of reproduction to slow down and there are more deaths in the population. When the birth rate and death rate are equal, the line of the graph becomes horizontal.

● **Try this** The answers are given on **p. 145**.

1 Figure 25.2 shows a population curve for a species of animal colonising a new habitat.

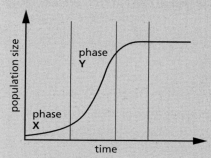

Figure 25.2

a) i) Identify phase **Y** of the curve. [1 mark]
   ii) Suggest why the population increase in phase **X** is slow. [2 marks]

b) Identify **three** factors that limit the size of such a population but do not appear to limit the total human population. [3 marks]

TOPIC 26 Human influences on the ecosystem

Key objectives

- To be able to discuss ways in which the use of modern technology has resulted in increased food production
- To be able to describe the undesirable effects of deforestation
- To be able to describe the overuse of fertilisers on the land
- To be able to describe the undesirable effects of water pollution by a range of pollutants
- To be able to describe the need for conservation of species and their habitats, and of natural resources
- To be able to assess the significance of non-biodegradable plastics and other materials used in manufacturing
- To be able to discuss the causes and apparent effects of acid rain, and ways of controlling it
- To be able to describe the principle of recycling materials

For this topic you need to emphasise examples of international importance such as rainforests, oceans and rivers.

Key ideas

How has the use of modern technology resulted in increased food production?

- Development and use of chemical fertilisers on farm land. These boost levels of nutrients in the soil, increasing crop yields.
- Development and use of pesticides such as insecticides and fungicides. These kill pests that feed on or damage crops, so crop yields are increased.
- Development and use of herbicides. These kill weeds that compete with crops for nutrients, light, water and space, so crop yields are increased.
- Development of biological control methods for pest control as an alternative to pesticides.
- Use of modern machinery, such as tractors and combine harvesters, has enabled land and crops to be managed more efficiently.
- Artificial selection to produce varieties of plants that are suited to particular climates and soil types, and breeds of animal for specific purposes such as optimum meat, milk, and wool production.
- Use of yeast and bacteria in the large-scale production of bread, beer and wine, yoghurt and cheese. Single-cell protein and fungi are used to produce meat substitutes.
- Use of medicines such as antibiotics, hormones and artificial insemination techniques in intensive animal rearing.
- Use of plant hormones in plant growing and fruit production.
- Use of genetic engineering and cloning techniques to produce organisms to produce hormones, etc.

- Development of systems to water plants in greenhouses automatically and to grow plants in nutrient solutions (a process called hydroponics).
- Use of satellites to monitor crop development, observe crop diseases and assess the need for additional fertiliser.
- Development of intensive farming and automated feeding mechanisms.

Undesirable effects of deforestation

Deforestation is the removal of large areas of forest to provide land for farming and roads, and to provide timber for building, furniture and fuel. Deforestation has a number of undesirable effects on the environment.

- Reduction of habitats or food sources for animals, which can result in their extinction. Animal and plant diversity is reduced, and food chains are disrupted.
- Loss of plant species and their genes which may be important for medical use or genetic engineering in the future.
- Removal of trees means there are no roots to hold soil, which can result in soil erosion and leaching of minerals. Desertification can eventually occur.
- Lack of roots and soil can lead to flooding and mudslides. Lakes can become silted up.
- Leaching of nutrients into lakes and rivers can lead to eutrophication.
- Less carbon dioxide is absorbed from the atmosphere, increasing the greenhouse effect.
- Less oxygen is produced, so atmospheric oxygen levels can drop.
- Less transpiration can lead to reduced rainfall.

● **Try this**   The answers are given on **p. 145**.

1 Figure 26.1 shows the area of tropical rainforest deforested annually in five different countries, labelled **A** to **E**.

a) i)   Which of the countries shown has the largest area deforested annually?   [1 mark]

   ii)   Which of the countries shown has 600 000 hectares of rainforest removed each year?   [1 mark]

   iii)   In another country, **F**, 550 000 hectares are deforested annually. Plot this on a copy of the figure.   [1 mark]

b) i)   Country **E** has a total of 9 000 000 hectares of tropical rainforest remaining. How long will it be before it is all destroyed, if the present rate of deforestation continues?   [1 mark]

   ii)   State **two** reasons why tropical rainforests are being destroyed by humans.   [2 marks]

   iii)   After deforestation has taken place, soil erosion often occurs rapidly. Suggest **two** ways in which this may occur.   [2 marks]

c)   Tropical rainforests reduce the amount of carbon dioxide and increase the amount of oxygen in the atmosphere. Explain why both these occurrences are important to living organisms.   [2 marks]

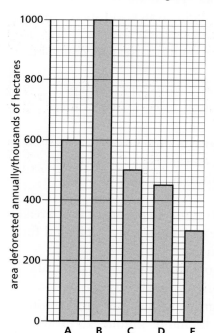

Figure 26.1

Overuse of fertilisers

It is very tempting for farmers to increase the amount of fertilisers applied to crops to try and increase crop yields. However, this can lead to the **eutrophication** of rivers and lakes, and the sequence in Figure 26.2 occurs.

A second effect of overuse of fertilisers can be the death of the plants. High concentrations of the fertiliser around plant roots can cause the roots to lose water by osmosis. The plant then wilts and dies.

Water pollution by sewage and chemical waste

Sewage can result in eutrophication in a similar way to overuse of fertilisers. This is because sewage contains high levels of nutrients such as phosphates, organic matter and bacteria. The phosphates act as fertilisers for algae, while the bacteria feed on the organic matter and reproduce rapidly, using up oxygen in respiration. If sewage is untreated before disposal it can lead to disease organisms such as cholera and typhoid being transmitted in the water.

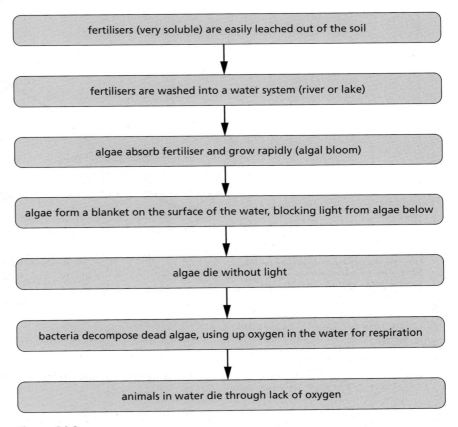

Figure 26.2

● **Try this** The answers are given on **p. 145**.

2 Figure 26.3a shows part of a river into which sewage is pumped. The river water flows from **W** to **Z**, with the sewage being added at **X**.

Some of the effects of adding sewage to the river are shown in Figure 26.3b.

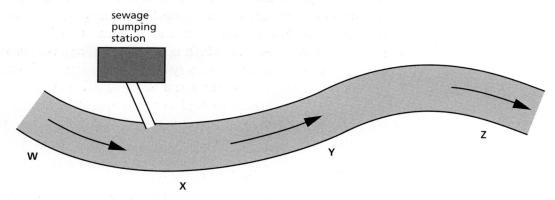

Figure 26.3a

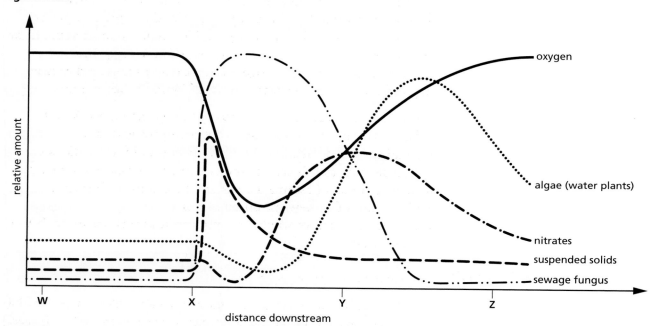

Figure 26.3b

a) Describe the changes in the levels from **W** to **Z** of:
   i)   nitrates   [2 marks]
   ii) suspended solids.   [2 marks]

b) Suggest why the level of oxygen:
   i)   drops at **X**   [1 mark]
   ii) increases again towards **Z**.   [1 mark]

c) Suggest **two** reasons why levels of algae drop:
   i)   when sewage is added to the river   [2 marks]
   ii) towards **Z**.   [2 marks]

d) A farm at **Z** used herbicides on the field next to the river.
   Suggest why this could cause further problems in the river.   [1 mark]

Chemical waste such as heavy metals (mercury, nickel, etc.) and oil can cause serious pollution. Some chemicals may be dumped (or enter water systems through leaching) in low concentrations, at which levels they are not toxic. However, bioaccumulation occurs if they enter a food chain. Plankton absorb the chemical and have no mechanism for excreting it. Animals such as small fish, feeding on large numbers of plankton, build up the chemical because, again, they have no means of excreting it. Animals, including humans, at the top of the food chain eat many fish and accumulate high concentrations of the chemical, which is now toxic. Poisons such as mercury damage the central nervous system and can lead to death.

When oil is dumped into water it can form a surface layer, coating animals such as birds that feed in the water. When the birds try to clean their feathers they swallow the oil, which poisons them. Oil also disrupts food chains.

Air pollution by sulphur dioxide

Sulphur dioxide is released into the air when coal and oil are burned. Power stations burn large amounts of these fossil fuels. Sulphur dioxide dissolves in the water vapour in clouds, forming sulphuric acid. When it rains, the rain is acidic. The combustion of petrol in car engines also contributes to acid rain, but this is mainly due to the production of oxides of nitrogen in the exhaust fumes, rather than sulphur dioxide. Problems caused by acid rain include the following.

- Damage to plant leaves, eventually killing the plants. Whole forests of pine trees have been destroyed by acid rain.
- Acidification of lakes: as the water becomes more acidic, some animals such as fish cannot survive and fish stocks are destroyed.
- Increased risk of asthma attacks and bronchitis in humans.
- Corrosion of stonework on buildings.
- Release into soil of soluble aluminium ions that are toxic to fish when washed into lakes.

● **Try this**   The answers are given on **pp. 145–6**.

3 a) Sulphur dioxide is a major pollutant of the air. Which process is mainly responsible for the release of sulphur dioxide into the air?   [1 mark]

b) Sulphur dioxide is one of the gases which contributes to acid rain. Acid rain can affect trees and their surrounding soil in a variety of ways. Figure 26.4 shows where these effects can occur.

Suggest how each of the following affects the tree and explain how it can lead to its death.
i) Damage to the leaves.   [2 marks]
ii) Damage to the fine roots.   [2 marks]
iii) Death of soil microorganisms.   [2 marks]

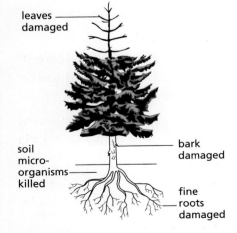

leaves damaged

soil micro-organisms killed

bark damaged

fine roots damaged

Figure 26.4

Pesticides, herbicides and nuclear fallout

Some **pesticides** are non–biodegradable and stay in the environment for a long time. For example, DDT has been a very effective insecticide, used to kill mosquitoes to reduce the spread of malaria. However, because it does not break down, it enters water systems such as lakes, where it is absorbed into plankton. They are unable to excrete DDT. In a similar way to heavy metals, it is passed up the food chain and bioaccumulation occurs: the top carnivores suffer from its toxicity. For example, when fish eagles are exposed to DDT passed through the food chain, they produce eggs with very thin shells. When the adult birds sit on the nest, the eggs break, so they are unable to produce offspring. Some insecticides are non–specific: when applied to kill an insect pest, they also kill all the other insects that are exposed to it. This may include useful insects, such as bees that are needed to pollinate crops. Food webs can be affected, threatening the extinction of top carnivores such as birds of prey.

Herbicides are used to kill weeds in a crop, to reduce competition to increase crop yield. However, herbicides may also kill rare plant species near the field being sprayed.

Nuclear fallout can be the result of a leak from a nuclear power station, or from a nuclear explosion. Radioactive particles are carried by the wind or water and gradually settle in the environment. If the radiation has a long half–life, it remains in the environment and is absorbed by living organisms. The radioactive material bioaccumulates in food chains and can cause cancer in top carnivores.

Non-biodegradable plastics

Plastics that are non–biodegradable are not broken down by decomposers when dumped in landfill sites or left as litter. This means they remain in the environment, taking up valuable space or causing visual pollution. Discarded plastic bottles can trap small animals; nylon fishing lines and nets can trap birds and mammals such as seals and dolphins. When plastic is burned it can release toxic gases.

Acid rain

The main causes of acid rain are processes that release sulphur dioxide and oxides of nitrogen into the atmosphere. These include:

- burning of fossil fuels, such as coal and gas, by power stations
- combustion of petrol in car engines.

The effects of acid rain have already been listed earlier in this topic: these need to be known for both the Core and Extended curricula.

Ways of reducing the incidence of acid rain include:

- changing the types of power stations that generate electricity from coal and oil to gas or nuclear power, or using more renewable energy sources such as wind
- using 'scrubbers' in power station chimneys – these remove most of the sulphur dioxide present in the waste gases
- using catalytic converters in car exhausts – these convert oxides of nitrogen to harmless nitrogen.

Common misconceptions

Remember that car engines do **not** make large amounts of sulphur dioxide – but they are responsible for producing large amounts of oxides of nitrogen, carbon dioxide and carbon monoxide. ■

Examiner's tip
► When describing the effects of car exhaust fumes on the environment, don't make a list of the chemicals and then link them all to acid rain or global warming. Be specific: oxides of nitrogen lead to acid rain; carbon monoxide can reduce the ability of haemoglobin to carry oxygen; and carbon dioxide increases can lead to global warming.

Conservation

Reasons for **conserving species** include the following.

- Many species of animals and plants are in danger of extinction, due to factors such as habitat destruction, the introduction of other species, international trade and pollution.
- Loss of a species also means that its genes are lost: these may be important in the future for genetic engineering (e.g. to improve crops) and the production of useful chemicals such as medicines.
- The presence of rare species can be an important source of money for poor communities, through tourism.
- The species may play an important role in a food chain: its loss could endanger other species.

The **conservation of habitats** is equally as important as the conservation of individual species. If habitats are lost, so are the species that live in them, so habitat destruction poses the greatest threat to the survival of species. A habitat may be conserved by:

- using laws to protect the habitat
- using wardens to protect the habitat
- reducing or controlling public access to the habitat
- controlling factors, such as water drainage and grazing, that may otherwise contribute to destruction of the habitat.

Examiner's tip
► Try to use one or more **examples** of conservation of a species and of a natural habitat in the area or country where you live. Include reasons for the species and habitat you have chosen.

Some natural resources (the materials we take from the Earth) are not replaceable (renewable). For example, fossil fuels such as coal took millions of years to form. Increasing demands for energy are depleting these resources. One way of conserving these resources is to increase the use of renewable energy (wind farms, solar power, hydroelectric power, etc.). Another is to improve the efficiency of energy use (better insulation, smaller car engines, more public transport, etc.). Trees can be grown specifically for fuel, then replanted as they are cut down. In this way the greenhouse effect is not increased, and habitats can be maintained when tree felling is carefully managed.

The principle of recycling sewage (water) and paper

Sewage is mainly water, contaminated with organic material, solids, bacteria and minerals such as phosphates. In places where water is in short supply, the sewage is treated to provide water that is clean enough to drink. Any treated effluent that is returned to a water system such as a river will not cause problems such as eutrophication.

Figure 26.5 describes the treatment of sewage to provide clean water.

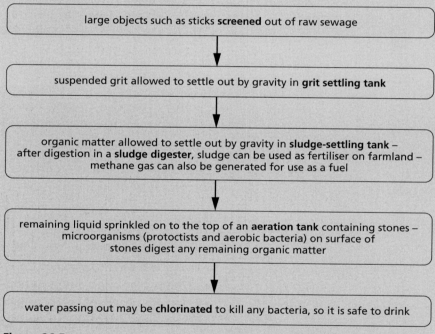

large objects such as sticks **screened** out of raw sewage

↓

suspended grit allowed to settle out by gravity in **grit settling tank**

↓

organic matter allowed to settle out by gravity in **sludge-settling tank** – after digestion in a **sludge digester**, sludge can be used as fertiliser on farmland – methane gas can also be generated for use as a fuel

↓

remaining liquid sprinkled on to the top of an **aeration tank** containing stones – microorganisms (protoctists and aerobic bacteria) on surface of stones digest any remaining organic matter

↓

water passing out may be **chlorinated** to kill any bacteria, so it is safe to drink

Figure 26.5

Paper is made from wood (trees). If the paper is recycled after use, fewer trees need to be cut down. The used paper is turned into a pulp and any dyes such as printing ink are removed. The pulp is then rolled into sheets and dried to produce recycled paper that can be used for newspapers, toilet paper, hand towels, etc.

Preparing for the examination

During the course

Preparing for an external examination is a continuous process throughout the course. All the activities, lessons, homework, practical work and assessments are major factors in determining the final examination grade, so the first piece of advice is to suggest that you work steadily throughout the two years of the course. It is essential that you prepare thoroughly for internal school examinations. Then, as you approach the IGCSE examination and start your revision programme, the topics will be familiar and the learning process will be less stressful and more productive.

Make sure that your notes are up to date. If you miss work through absence, either copy it from a friend or leave a comment in your notes that will remind you to refer to the topic in a textbook. Similarly, look at any homework you have missed and if it involves the reinforcement of skills or concepts, then it would be a good idea to photocopy the work from a friend. Do ask for help if there are parts of a topic you don't understand.

In summary you should do the following.

- Work steadily throughout the course.
- Ensure that your work is both complete and accurate.
- Learn the topics for tests and internal examinations.
- If you find an aspect of the course difficult, ask for help.

Revision techniques

Well in advance of the examination, produce a revision timetable for all your subjects, but be realistic and include time for relaxation and socialising. Then create a more detailed timetable for Biology, to cover all the topics. Use the topic list at the start of this book to help you divide the syllabus up into sections. Ideally, you should go through the complete course twice. Keep a checklist of the topics studied – keeping a visual record of your progress will help to motivate you.

It is useful to have a copy of the syllabus, but not essential, as this book includes all the information required for IGCSE Biology. You will need a quiet room at a comfortable temperature, plenty of paper, and a pencil or pen. Some students find background music creates a good atmosphere in which they can concentrate. On occasion, revising with a friend makes a welcome and useful change. You will have to discover for how long you can profitably study one subject at a time – this is a very individual characteristic and can vary from person to person. It may range from as little as 30 minutes to over an hour. Do not exceed your revision time, and break up the available time into study sessions and breaks. Generally, the brain becomes less effective after a revision period of about 20 minutes, so make sure you introduce short breaks with rewards – 'When I have finished this section of work I will …'. This could involve a five-minute break with a drink or a snack to allow you to switch off and refresh your brain for the next revision session. You could have three blocks of 20 minutes with short breaks, before changing to a different activity.

Revision must be active – just looking at a book is not an effective way of learning. You could make flash cards that have bullet lists of essential points. You could study the topic for several minutes and then close the book and write out what you can remember (without taking great care over presentation), then check your account against the information in the book. Repeat this process until you have most of the details correct, then move on to another section of the work. This is the 'look, cover, write and check' technique, and it is very effective for most students. It is crucial that you repeat this technique on the same topic at least once, but preferably twice – ideally later the same day or the next day. This will greatly increase your long-term retention of the work.

Keeping a list of important words and their definitions is useful. You could write the words on one side of a card and the meanings on the other. Then, when you have a few minutes to spare you can check up on your Biology vocabulary.

Once you have acquired a reasonably good knowledge and understanding of the course, it is time to extend the revision to practising on past papers. This is a most valuable form of preparation; not only does it provide a test of the effectiveness of your revision but it also provides an insight of what to expect in the 'real' examination.

How to approach the examination

If the examination centre has given you a detailed timetable, highlight your examinations and put the timetable in a prominent place in your home. Ask one of your family or a friend to check with you each day your commitments for the next day. This will help avoid last-minute panics.

Put out the correct equipment the night before – pencil, pencil sharpener, eraser, ruler, calculator (are the batteries OK?) and two pens.

If you are travelling to school, leave home in plenty of time; if you are late you will not be given extra time and under certain circumstances you will not be allowed to enter the examination room. The regulations vary depending on the Examination Board. It is the candidate's responsibility to arrive on time for the examination, and you should always allow time to spare.

Avoid doing last-minute revision, or revision just before you go to bed. This can cause you to forget previous information you have revised, and cause panic.

Multiple-choice papers

Attempt all of the questions – there are no penalties for incorrect responses.

Read the question carefully, remembering that at least one of the incorrect answers (called distractors) will seem to be correct. Do not rush – think.

If you cannot answer a question, or remain uncertain about which is the correct answer, put a mark by it in the margin of the paper, leave it, and return to it when you have completed the other questions. Try to avoid making a blind guess. Try to eliminate some of the incorrect answers, as this increases the odds of choosing the correct response in your favour. Use any spare time at the end of the examination to check your answers.

Theory papers

Once the examination has started, browse through the paper and choose a question you feel confident about. You do not have to start with question 1. Read the question twice, look at the mark allocation for each part and then decide exactly what is required to achieve the marks. This requires a disciplined approach; far too many candidates write at length without actually answering the question. Never forget – marks are not awarded for correct Biology, but for correct Biology that answers the question.

- Follow the instructions in the question, being particularly careful to respond to words and phrases such as 'describe' and 'explain'.
- Take reasonable care that your writing is legible – what cannot be read cannot be marked.
- Do not offer more alternative answers than are required by the question. This wastes valuable time, and the examiner will not pick out the correct answers from a long list.
- Avoid 'waffle', as this wastes your time. Plan your answer before writing it down, and do not rewrite the information given in the question.
- Do not rush – this is a major cause of mistakes, particularly of misreading the question. The time allocated to the examination is adequate for candidates to complete the paper.
- Leave the most difficult questions until last. Make sure you attempt all the questions.
- If you finish early, use the time to check through your answers. Ask yourself 'Have I answered the question and have I made sufficient points to be awarded all the marks?'.

After the examination, the papers are sent to the examiner allocated to your centre. This examiner will be part of a team headed by a Chief Examiner. All the members of the examining team will look at a sample of their scripts and assess the range of candidates' responses to each question. About a week after the examination, the team will meet to coordinate the marking. For each question, they will decide the range of responses that are acceptable. During the marking period, the Chief Examiner will sample the marking of each examiner at least twice, to ensure comparability of marking across the team. The scripts and the marks are returned to the Examination Board, where the minimum mark for each grade is decided. A few weeks later you are informed of your grade.

Practical examinations

There are three ways of assessing practical skills.

School-based assessment (course work)

A series of assessments are conducted throughout the course, and should be an integral part of the teaching programme. The teachers will have received guidance and training about the conduct and content of these assessments. The following skills will be assessed.

C1 Using and organising techniques, apparatus and materials.
C2 Observing, measuring and recording.
C3 Interpreting and evaluating experimental observations and data.
C4 Planning, carrying out and evaluating investigations.

Near the end of the course, the results of these assessments are sent to the Examination Board where they are moderated, to keep the same standard across all the centres.

Practical test

This is a single practical test set by the Examination Board and conducted at your centre. The procedures assessed are the same as those in the school-based assessment. This paper is marked by external examiners.

Written test of practical skills (alternative to practical)

This is a part of the final examination programme. It is a single written paper devoted entirely to laboratory procedures. The syllabus gives a complete list of the required procedures, which include:

- following a series of instructions
- using techniques to record observations
- recalling physiological experiments
- recognising biological specimens
- making line drawings from photographs of specimens
- calculating the magnification of a drawing
- recording readings from diagrams of apparatus
- completing tables of data
- drawing conclusions
- plotting graphs
- identifying sources of error and suggesting improvements in experimental procedures.

These papers are marked by a team of external examiners in the same way as the theory papers.

Preparation for practical assessment

The best preparation for the written test is to study some of the past papers to become familiar with the type of question set. It is likely that that the questions on your paper will be similar. Although it is a written test, the practical lessons at school will have provided both the skills and knowledge needed for this examination.

The two direct assessments of practical skills (the school-based assessment and the practical test) present different problems from a purely written assessment – in a word, nerves. In any examination you need to be calm and measured in your approach. This is certainly easier to achieve in the written examination – a couple of deep breaths, pick a question you are confident about and 'off you go'. If you make a mistake, you can just delete it and write the correct version (with a reference to the examiner) in a convenient place. This is not the case for practical work. You will probably have to start the exercise again if you make a mistake, assuming there is enough material. You will have wasted time, and not improved your state of mind. In a practical examination, think about what you are about to do, and when you are certain of the correct action, carry it out. Do not rush.

How to improve your grade

Here are a few brief summary points, all of which have been mentioned elsewhere in this book.

- Use this book – it has been written to help students achieve high grades.
- Learn all the work – low grades are nearly always attributable to inadequate preparation. If you can recall the work, you will succeed. Don't leave things to chance.
- Practise skills such as calculations, equation writing, labelling diagrams and the interpretation of graphs.
- Use past papers to reinforce revision, to become familiar with the type of question and to gain confidence.
- Answer the question as instructed on the paper – be guided by the key words used in the question (describe, explain, list, etc.). Do not accept a question as an invitation to write about the topic.

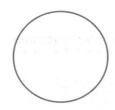

Answers to 'Try this' questions

Topic 1

1 i) nutrition
   ii) respiration
   iii) movement
   iv) excretion

Topic 2

1 One possible mnemonic is: Bees Prefer Finding Pollen Alone.

2 A fish; **B** amphibian; **C** mammal; **D** bird; **E** reptile

3 i), ii) Suitable features, as listed in Figure 2.2 exoskeleton; segmented body; jointed limbs

4 a) i) Plants
   ii) Any **two** answers from:
   – fungi do not have chlorophyll (or cannot photosynthesise)
   – fungi do not always have cellulose cell walls (or fungi have cell walls with chitin)
   – fungi have hyphae or produce a mycelium.

   b) i) $56.3/64.4 \times 100 = 87.4\%$
   ii) There are a number of features you could choose from, including wings, cuticle (or exoskeleton), three pairs of legs, compound eyes.
   An explanation for wings would be: being able to fly to find food or a mate, or to escape from predators.

   c) i) The presence of a beak or feathers.
   ii) The presence of scales, eyes, tail, mouth or anus.

   d) $1\,700\,000/100 \times 14.3 = 243\,100$

Topic 3

1

Leaf	1a	1b	2a	2b	3a	3b	4a	4b	5a	5b	Name of tree
B		✓				✓				✓	*Quercus*
C		✓				✓			✓		*Ilex*
D		✓		✓				✓			*Fraxinus*
E		✓			✓		✓				*Aesculus*
F	✓			✓							*Magnolia*

Topic 4

1 Drawings should be suitably labelled.

Topic 5

1 A, upper epidermis. **Two** details from:
   – a single layer of cells
   – produces or secretes wax or cuticle
   – to make leaf waterproof
   – reference to transparent nature of cells
   – to allow light to pass through
   – reference to acting as a barrier against bacteria or fungi.

   B, palisade mesophyll. **Two** details from:
   – cells are very long or columnar
   – cells contain chloroplasts or chlorophyll
   – reference to photosynthesis.

   C, spongy mesophyll. **Two** details from:
   – cells are rounded
   – air spaces are present between cells
   – reference to photosynthesis
   – reference to gaseous exchange.

   D, guard cells. **Two** details from:
   – present in pairs
   – guard cells surround a stomatal pore
   – control the opening or closing of the pore
   – reference to gaseous exchange
   – reference to control of transpiration.

2 Width from **A** to **B** = 7.5 cm (or 75 mm) magnification = observed size/actual size, so actual size = observed size/magnification
= 7.5/2.5 = 3.0 cm (or 30 mm)

Topic 6

1 **a)** **Two** points from:
- reference to large numbers
- cells have a large surface (area)
- mitochondria are present to provide energy.

b) **i)** **Two** points from:
- absorption of a substance into a cell or across a membrane
- against or up a concentration gradient
- reference to the process using energy.

ii) Active transport requires energy.

Topic 7

1 **a)** **i)** The volume of water in the dish decreased.

ii) The volume of salt solution in the potato increased.

b) **i)** osmosis

ii) **Three** points from:
- there was a higher concentration of water in the dish than in the potato (or there was a higher concentration of salt in the potato than in the dish)
- so water moved into the potato
- from a high concentration of water to a lower concentration of water
- by osmosis.

iii) Root hairs, or in the roots.

iv) Osmosis enables the plant to absorb water to maintain cell turgidity (or to replace water lost by transpiration).

Topic 8

1

Name of enzyme	Substrate (what the enzyme works on)	End-product(s)	Other details, e.g. where reaction happens, optimum pH
salivary amylase	starch	maltose, glucose	mouth, pH 6.8
protease	protein	amino acids	stomach, pH 2 duodenum, pH 9
pancreatic lipase	fat	fatty acids, glycerol	duodenum, pH 9

2 **a)** x axis with temperature with suitable scale (0–50 or 15–50°C), and label with units. y axis with time from 0–35 or 0–40 minutes, and label with units. All points plotted accurately and line drawn to link points on the graph.

b) **i)** One way is to take small samples of the mixture at regular time intervals and test these with iodine solution. When all the starch has been digested, the mixture will not turn blue–black (an orange/brown colour would appear).

ii) 35°C

iii) As the temperature is increased from 15 to 35°C the rate of starch digestion increases. From 35 to 50°C the rate of starch digestion decreases.

c) **i)** The starch would be digested very quickly (in about 3 minutes) because exposure to the low temperature would not affect the enzyme, just slow down its action.

ii) The starch would not be digested at all, because exposure to the high temperature would denature the enzyme. This effect is permanent.

3 **a)** **i)** Blood contains proteins, so trypsin will be needed to digest them.

ii) amino acids

iii) **One** suitable use such as: for growth; the production of enzymes; or the formation of muscle or cell membranes.

b) The mosquitoes would starve to death, because they would not be able to digest the proteins in the blood they feed on.

c) Boiling it or heating it; exposing it to extreme pH.

Topic 9

1 See page 28 for suitable details.

Topic 10

1

Part of leaf	Results of starch test	Reason
A	Negative – orange/brown	No light to photosynthesise, so no starch produced
B	Positive – blue/black	Light and chlorophyll to photosynthesise, so starch is produced
C	Negative – orange/brown	No chlorophyll to photosynthesise, so no starch produced
D	Negative – orange/brown	No light or chlorophyll to photosynthesise, so no starch produced

2 a) i) Curve A, because the rate of sugar production is higher due to a higher rate of photosynthesis.

　　ii) Chloroplasts contain chlorophyll, which traps sunlight.

　　iii) One answer from:
　　　　– thickness of the leaf
　　　　– transparency of the leaf
　　　　– angle of the leaf to the light.

　b) i) Starch is insoluble so it stays where it is stored.

　　ii) Iodine solution.

3 a) $300/150 \times 100 = 200\%$

　b) Container **A**: **one** suggestion such as:
　　– depletion of salts or nutrients
　　– release of seeds
　　– effects of disease
　　– shortage of carbon dioxide
　　– end of the plant's life cycle.
　　Container **B**: **one** suggestion such as:
　　– nutrients still available
　　– photosynthesis or growth
　　– food stored
　　– plenty of carbon dioxide available.

　c) Container **C**. **One** point from:
　　– least photosynthesis happening
　　– respiration is happening faster than photosynthesis
　　– the plant has died, so bacteria feed on it, using up oxygen.

　d) Green or blue. **One** point from:
　　– little or no photosynthesis is happening
　　– no light absorbed by chlorophyll
　　– no sugars (or starch) made.

4 One mark for each statement (as on the table on page 34).

5 a) i) Making proteins or amino acids.

　　ii) Two points from:
　　　　– it makes the crops grow bigger or more quickly
　　　　– so the profits are increased
　　　　– the previous crops will have removed much of the nitrates in the soil
　　　　– nitrates are leached out of the soil.

　b) Five points from:
　　– the pond plants will grow faster
　　– plants on the surface will block the light for plants below
　　– plants die
　　– bacteria will feed on the dead plants
　　– bacteria respire, using up oxygen
　　– animals die due to lack of oxygen.

Topic 11

1 Any useful mnemonic such as **C**an **F**lowers **P**ollinate **V**ery **M**uch (in) **F**reezing **W**inters?

Topic 12

1 a) Incisor, canine, premolar and molar tooth labelled in the correct places.

　b) i) Biting or cutting food.

　　ii) Chewing or grinding or crushing food.

　c) i) Enamel

　　ii) Mineral: calcium; vitamin: D.

　　iii) Three points from:
　　　　– bacteria feed on sugar from food left on the teeth
　　　　– bacteria produce acid
　　　　– acid attacks or dissolves the enamel
　　　　– dentine is softer, so it breaks down more quickly
　　　　– this results in a hole in the enamel, exposing the pulp cavity.

Topic 13

1 a) Labels should include cell wall, membrane, nucleus, cytoplasm, sap vacuole.

　b) Chloroplast

　c) i) Osmosis

　　ii) Diffusion or active transport (or active uptake).

2 a) **A**, stoma or stomatal pore; **B**, guard cell; **C**, epidermal cell or epidermis.

　b) *C. fistula* has stomata on upper surface and *B. monandra* has stomata on lower surface. *B. monandra* has more stomata than *C. fistula* (or you could compare the figures).

c) i) **Three** points from:
- colour change is due to water loss
- water lost through the stomata
- stomata are open during the day
- reference to transpiration.

  ii) **One** point from:
- stomata or guard cells are closed at night
- there is no transpiration or no water loss at night.

d) **Three** points from:
- reference to xylem or tracheids
- water enters xylem vessel through pits in walls
- reference to osmosis (for absorption of water)
- reference to transpiration stream or transpiration pull
- reference to capillary action or to the cohesion of water molecules
- reference to root pressure.

e) i) The rate will decrease. **One** point from:
- there is a smaller gradient
- reference to diffusion.

  ii) The rate will increase. **One** point from:
- more energy or heat for evaporation
- water evaporates more quickly at higher temperatures
- warm air can hold more water vapour than cold air.

Topic 14

1 Correctly labelled diagram and shading.
2 a) i) Labels correctly placed for the pulmonary artery, pulmonary vein, vena cava and aorta.

  ii) Labels correctly placed for left atrium, left ventricle, right atrium and right ventricle.

  iii) Tricuspid valve (between right atrium and right ventricle); bicuspid valve (between left atrium and left ventricle).

b) Blood leaving the right ventricle has more carbon dioxide and less oxygen than blood entering the left atrium.

Topic 15

1 Wall of alveolus – one cell thick (or very thin) so that diffusion happens quickly.
Moist surface – allows oxygen to dissolve making diffusion faster.

Blood is moving – so that a concentration gradient is maintained for oxygen and carbon dioxide.
Wall of capillary – one cell thick (or very thin) so that diffusion happens quickly.
Red blood cells – contain haemoglobin to transport oxygen away from the lungs.

2 a) i) Inspired air contains more oxygen, less carbon dioxide and less water vapour than expired air.

  ii) **Three** features from:
- the wall of the alveolus is one cell thick (or very thin)
- there is a moist surface to the alveoli
- there are large numbers of alveoli
- the air in the alveoli is constantly being replaced.

b) i) The release of energy by cells without the use of oxygen.

  ii) In muscle cells.

3 **Breathing in:**
- external intercostal muscles contract
- ribcage moves upwards and outwards
- the diaphragm muscles contract
- the diaphragm moves down
- the volume of the thorax increases
- the air pressure in the thoracic cavity reduces
- air rushes into the lungs through the mouth or nose.

For **breathing out**, the descriptions are the opposite of breathing in.

Topic 17

1 a) i) Positive phototropism.

  ii) **Three** points from:
- the coleoptiles have been exposed to one-sided light
- auxins have been produced by the tip
- and have passed into the block
- auxins have passed from the block to the cut coleoptile
- more auxin accumulates on the shaded side of the coleoptile
- causing more growth on the shaded side.

b) **A**, taller and growing vertically upwards;
B, taller and bending towards the light;
C, taller and growing vertically upwards.

c) i) Taxis (or taxic response).
   ii) Four points from:
   – it helps them to avoid predators
   – there are food sources in dark places
   – water sources are present in dark places
   – it helps the animals to avoid dehydration
   – it is cooler in the dark
   – it helps the animals to avoid harmful ultraviolet rays.

Topic 18

1 a) Contract; pull
   b) Muscles **A and B**; and **C and D** are antagonistic pairs. They have opposite effects when they contract.
   c) i) C
      ii) B
   d) i) Anaerobic respiration.
      ii) Lactic acid (or lactate).
2 a) i) Motor neurone.
      ii) Two features from:
      – presence of motor end plates
      – the cell body is at the beginning of the cell
      – the cell body has dendrites on
      – there is no dendron (only an axon).
      iii) Peripheral nervous system.
   b) Cytoplasm: **two** suggestions from:
      – is elongated
      – passes electrical signals along
      – connects different parts of the body
      – is modified to form dendrites.
      Myelin sheath: **two** suggestions from:
      – acts as insulating material
      – so prevents leakage of electrical signal from axon
      – allows faster transmission of impulses.
   c) i) Stimulus, receptor, coordinator, effector, response
      ii) Effector: iris (muscle).
      Receptor: retina or rods or cones.
      Response: pupil changes diameter or iris muscles contract.
      Stimulus: bright light or change in light intensity.
3 Suitably labelled diagrams.
4 – ciliary muscles contract
   – the suspensory ligaments become relaxed
   – so tension is removed from the lens
   – the lens becomes more convex
   – so light is focused more strongly

5 Speed, slow(er).
Pathway, bloodstream.
Nature, electrical.
Origin, sense organ/brain.
6 a) i) Depressant: a drug which acts on the central nervous system, leading to relaxation and sleep or unconsciousness.
   Addictive: causes the development of dependence on a drug.
      ii) Two long-term effects such as:
      – liver damage (cirrhosis)
      – brain damage
      – alcoholism
      – stomach ulcers
      – obesity.
   b) The performance will reduce as the amount of alcohol drunk is increased. Reactions will be slower due to decreased coordination, resulting in a greater risk of accidents.
7 Glucose, pancreas, secretion, glycogen, insulin, liver.

Topic 19

1 a) A, ovule; **B**, sepal.
   b) C (petals) are large and colourful to attract insects; **D** (stigma) is sticky and lies in the way of the insects to collect pollen; **E** (anther) produces pollen and lies in the way of the insects to transfer pollen on to their bodies.
   c) Four points from:
      – pollen grains germinate
      – pollen tube grows down the style
      – through the micropyle
      – into the ovule
      – the male nucleus fuses with the female nucleus
      – reference to fertilisation.
2 a) i) A, plumule; **B**, cotyledon; **C**, testa (seed coat).
      ii) X on any part of the cotyledon.
   b) i) Sketch of a wind-dispersed fruit or seed such as dandelion or sycamore. **Y** on the part that catches the wind (such as parachute or wing).
      ii) Two points from:
      – description of how the feature catches the wind
      – and slows down the descent of the seed or fruit

   – so the seed or fruit is carried away from the parent plant.

   iii) Wind pollination.

3 a) i) Stores food.

   ii) B develops into the shoot (or leaves); **C** develops into the root.

b) i) Wet mass varies according to the amount of water absorbed or lost from the plant, or dry mass represents the amount of cytoplasm.

   ii) Four points from:
   – the dry mass drops between days **X** and **Y** for both sets of seedlings
   – food stored in the cotyledons
   – is used to supply energy
   – through respiration
   – some food is converted into other materials
   – for growth of the radical and plumule.

   iii) Four points from:
   – set **Q** increases in dry mass and set **P** decreases in mass
   – set **Q** is in the light and can photosynthesise
   – to make new cytoplasm
   – set **P** is in the dark and cannot photosynthesise
   – set **P** uses up remaining food stores through respiration.

Topic 20

1 a) i) A, umbilical cord; **B**, vagina.

   ii) Three functions from:
   – transfers oxygen from mother to fetus
   – transfers nutrients (or named nutrients) from mother to fetus
   – transfers carbon dioxide from fetus to mother
   – transfers wastes (or named wastes) from fetus to mother
   – allows the transfer of antibodies from mother to fetus
   – prevents mixing of the blood of mother and fetus.

   iii) Helps prevent bacteria passing from mother to fetus; the blood groups of mother and fetus may be different.

2 Three points from:
   – the wall of the uterus contracts
   – the amniotic sac bursts
   – amniotic fluid passes out through the vagina

   – the cervix dilates
   – the baby passes out through the cervix and vagina.

3 a) i) Sperm duct labelled correctly between the testes and urethra.

   ii) Urethra labelled correctly between bladder and tip of penis.

b) In males the urethra carries urine and semen at different times; in females the urethra only carries urine.

c) i) Two male secondary sexual characteristics from:
   – voice becomes much lower (breaks)
   – hair starts to grow on chest, face, under arms and pubic area
   – body becomes more muscular
   – penis becomes larger
   – testes start to produce sperm.

   ii) Testis (or testes) labelled correctly.

   iii) Testosterone makes muscles grow, so the athletes can run faster or perform better.

4 i) Two points from:
   – using an unsterilised, used needle (in drug-taking or blood sampling)
   – unprotected sex with an infected person
   – receiving a blood transfusion containing infected blood
   – having a tattoo or body piercing using an unsterilised, used needle.

   ii) Two harmful materials from:
   – drugs such as heroin
   – paracetamol or aspirin
   – nicotine
   – alcohol.

Topic 21

1 a) Ciliated cell: 46; red blood cell: 0 (this cell has no nucleus); ovum: 23.

b) Two differences from:
   – chromosomes in daughter mitotic cells will be identical to parental chromosomes (or there is no variation)
   – genes in daughter mitotic cells will be identical to parental genes
   – chromosomes in daughter mitotic cells will be in homologous pairs, but they will be single in meiotic nuclei.

2 a) Rr

   b) rr

   c) RR

3 Gene, meiosis, diploid, phenotype, recessive, heterozygous.

4 A cross between two pink-flowering plants. The genotype of both plants must be C^RC^W

phenotypes of parents	**pink**	**pink**
genotypes of parents	C^RC^W ×	C^RC^W
gametes	C^R C^W ×	C^R C^W

punnett square

	C^R	C^W
C^R	C^RC^R	C^RC^W
C^W	C^RC^W	C^WC^W

F_1 genotypes	1 C^RC^R, 2 C^RC^W, 1 C^WC^W,		
F_1 phenotypes	**red**	**pink**	**white**
Ratio	1 red	2 pink	1 white

Topic 22

1 a) $56/70 \times 100 = 80\%$

   b) i) Continuous variation.

     ii) Any **three** factors from: genes, temperature, disease, seed size, light, oxygen, carbon dioxide, water, minerals, mutation, trampling by animals.

2 a) A method used by humans to produce varieties of animals and plants which have an increased economic importance.

   b) i) Any endangered species, such as panda, tiger, elephant, named whale species, named tuna species.

     ii) Two points from:
        – to maintain the gene pool
        – to provide chemicals that may be useful in development of medicines
        – the species may be an important part of a food chain
        – rare species may provide tourism to supply poor communities with money.

Topic 23

1 a) A *producer* is an organism that makes its own food using energy from sunlight through the process of photosynthesis; a *consumer* is an organism that obtains its food by feeding on other organisms.

   b) A *carnivore* is an animal that eats other animals; a *herbivore* is an animal that eats plants.

2 a) i) Light (or solar) energy.
     ii) Chemical energy.

   b) i) 1200 units
     ii) 48 units

   c) i) The consumer may be warm-blooded, so some energy is lost as heat. Consumers usually move around to find food, a mate, or escape from predators, which uses up energy, but producers do not move.

     ii) Feeding as a first consumer involves eating plants. Less energy is lost to the environment when feeding at this level, so food production is more efficient in terms of energy conservation.

3 a)

Two organisms from:	Consumer	Producer	Carnivore	Herbivore
	Bank voles	Grass	Wrens	Bank voles
	Goldfinches	Hogweed	Kestrels	Goldfinches
	Aphids	Ivy		Aphids
	Caterpillars	Oak tree		Caterpillars
	Wrens			
	Kestrels			

   b) Six suggestions such as:
     – decrease in aphids because ladybirds eat aphids
     – increase in ivy because there will be fewer aphids feeding
     – decrease in wrens because there are fewer aphids to eat
     – decrease in caterpillars because the wrens now have only caterpillars for food
     – increase in oak trees because there will be fewer aphids feeding
     – increase in hogweed because there will be fewer aphids feeding
     – increase in goldfinches because there is more hogweed to eat.

Note that there are other possible suggestions.

Topic 24

1 a) A, carbon compounds in plants; **B**, carbon compounds in dead plants and animals.

   b) i) C on arrow between fossil fuels and carbon dioxide in the air.
     ii) D on arrow between box **B** and carbon dioxide in the air.
     iii) P on arrow between carbon dioxide in the air and box **A**.

iv) R on arrow between carbon compounds in animals (or box **A**) and carbon dioxide in the air.

2 a) i) Proteins (or amino acids).
  ii) Urea or ammonia or uric acid.
  iii) Bacteria
  iv) Lightning or electrical storms.

  b) Four points from:
  – aerated soils allow the activity of useful bacteria
  – to convert ammonium compounds into nitrites
  – and to convert nitrites into nitrates
  – nitrates can be absorbed by plants
  – to allow growth or formation of proteins
  – waterlogged soils encourage denitrifying bacteria
  – which break down nitrates into nitrogen
  – so there would be a shortage of nitrates for plants to absorb
  – leading to poor growth.

Topic 25

1 a) i) Log phase (or exponential phase).
  ii) The new population is taking time to settle or mature, before breeding begins. When this happens, a doubling of small numbers does not have a big impact on the total population size, so the line of the graph rises only slowly with time.

  b) Three factors from:
  – amount of food available
  – disease
  – space
  – predation.

Topic 26

1 a) i) B
  ii) A
  iii) Column for **F** drawn to 550. Column shaded in the same way as the others, and labelled. Column drawn an equal width and distance from the others.

  b) i) 30 years.
  ii) Two reasons from:
  – to clear land for agriculture, housing, industry or roads

– to collect timber for housing
– to collect timber for fuel.
  iii) Two suggestions from:
  – plants have gone so there are no roots to bind the soil
  – wind blows soil away
  – rain washes soil away.

  c) Increased carbon dioxide can lead to global warming, or flooding, or desertification.
  Oxygen: organisms need oxygen for respiration to release energy.

2 a) i) Constant level between **W** and **X**, or starts off quite low, or at point **X** it starts to drop then increases towards **Y** before dropping again towards **Z**
  ii) Level starts off quite low, then at point **X** it increases sharply; level returns nearly to original level between **Y** and **Z**

  b) i) One suggestion from:
  – aerobic respiration by sewage fungus
  – lack of algae to produce oxygen.
  ii) One suggestion from:
  – lack of sewage fungus
  – photosynthesis by algae.

  c) i) Two suggestions from:
  – presence of suspended solids blocks light for algae
  – lack of nitrate in the water
  – possible presence of toxins in sewage
  – possible increase in temperature or unsuitable temperature.
  ii) Two suggestions from:
  – shortage of nitrates
  – grazing by aquatic herbivores
  – possible drop in temperature, or unsuitable temperature.

  d) One suggestion from:
  – herbicides could leach into river and kill algae
  – herbicides will kill algae and disrupt food chains
  – herbicides may be toxic to other organisms in the river.

3 a) Combustion of fossil fuels.
  b) i) The leaves are unable to photosynthesise, so it cannot make food.

ii) One suggestion and explanation from:
- the roots are unable to absorb water, so cells will become flaccid, or the tree will wilt, or transport of materials will not happen
- the roots are unable to absorb mineral salts which are needed, e.g. for formation of chlorophyll, or for growth.

iii) One suggestion and explanation from:
- less decomposition will occur, so there will be less minerals available to the plant, e.g. magnesium ions for formation of chlorophyll
- there will be no nitrogen-fixing bacteria, so there will be less nitrates for the roots to take up, which are needed for protein formation.

Index

Note: page numbers in *italics* refer to definitions of terms.